AN
ASSEMBLAGE
of WRITINGS *by* THE
STUDENTS *of*
826CHI

VOLUME 3

CONTENTS

◐ Workshops △ Field-Trips ▥ In-Schools
▲ After-School Tutoring and Writing ◈ At-Large Submissions

Please note that these symbols reflect the 826CHI
programmatic origin for each piece.

PREFACE

Welcome to the third volume of the 826CHI *Compendium*; the
volume that officially moves your ongoing *Compendium*
collection from "company" to "a crowd." A perceptive, thoughtful and entertaining crowd to be sure. This new collection, like
its predecessors, features spectacularly written pieces that will
set you laughing, pondering, crying, and reminiscing. They
will hopefully inspire you to write as well.

For those readers new to the *Compendium*, who have forgotten,
or who love to read things already known, this book's contents
are culled from pieces written by 826CHI writers who share at
least these three things in common: they are human, they have
been on the earth for 6 to 18 years, and they live in Chicago.

The authors produced these pieces through programs at
826CHI, a nonprofit, volunteer-powered, creative writing and

tutoring center that, like most writing and tutoring centers, is housed behind a secret agent supply store. For more information about 826CHI and its programs, you can flip to the back of the book or just whisper, "Can you please explain the programs and did you really mean that secret agent thing?" As spies, we've bugged this book and will be at your doorstep momentarily to tell you all about what we do.

Please bear in mind that this is not the sum total of the great pieces written at 826CHI over the past year or so. If that were the case, your hand would break from the weight of the book and we most certainly would have been forced to deplete an irresponsibly large quantity of forests for its production.

As such, we whittled down the contents to a safe and sustainable size, arranged in reverse alphabetical order by title. The students found their muse in family, zombies, and Michael Jackson; we found ours for the sequencing of the book in the "Cha Cha Slide." Amidst all the stomping, hopping, and criss-crossing, DJ Casper intones the listener rather emphatically to: Reverse! As such we went from a-z, to z-a; flipping the order.

Now, this is our third *Compendium* and that number is significant. Three, as triangle designers and table makers know, implies stability. We decided to honor this inherent steadiness by inviting you to its opposite: chaos. Though the book is arranged in the aforementioned order, and can certainly be read that way, we highly encourage you to embrace an unknown sequence.

But how to go about your random reading process? If the classic method of thumbing through the pages and haphazardly jabbing your index finger onto a page does not sound appealing and the threat of a paper-cut too high, here are but three other (non-finger) tips to finding just that right story to read:

1. Stop a stranger on the street. Ask her what her shoe size is. Multiply by 3. Go to that page and enjoy.

2. See how high you can count, out loud, during a standardized test, wedding, or jury duty before someone requests that you stop. Turn to the page that corresponds to the number and enjoy!

3. Take your age. Add your favorite professional athlete's number to it. Multiply by 14. Then, add 3. Forget that number and turn to page 66 and enjoy!

In short, adventurously leap about. Commence your *Compendium* reading experience immediately. Time is too precious and the writing within too good to miss.

Happy reading!

COMPENDIUM

vol 3

Zombies Can Play Video Games

BY Parker Ljung, *Grade 4*
FROM *Zombies Can't Write, But Kids Can!, Spring 2010*

ONCE UPON A TIME, there was a zombie named Joe-Bob. He 17
found *Left 4 Dead* in an Xbox in his house and started to play
it. He beat the whole game without even trying. He kept
beating it until he saw his cousin in the game. He stopped
playing it and went to costumer service to tell the people
not to make zombie-killing games. They stopped making
the video games because Joe-Bob threatened to sue them for
9.1 trillion dollars.

Zombie Attack

BY Amalia Pappa, *Grade 2*
FROM *25 Seconds to Eat the Whole Pie, Spring 2011*

IT WAS A GLOOMY-NIGHT midnight when the zombies came out. I was still awake, and then—footsteps. Who was it?

ZOMBIES! But guess who was brave. OK, maybe not me, but I knew who was. Justin Bieber? No. Rahm Emanuel? No. Ghosts? Yes! I knew it all along. So I called the ghost family: 892-555-8118.

The girls, boys, mom, and dad picked up. They said, "HellooOOoo."

I said, "Hey."

They said, "Is that youuuu, Amalia?"

I said, "Yeah. I need your help."

"Sureee," they said.

"OK. Zombies are at my house—come as fast as you can."

So they came.

I wasn't freaked out. I knew the ghosts and they were friendly. I would let them in, but I knew they would just go through the walls. I was correct. But the zombies were coming closer. I was running out of time.

I said, "Get your zinger guns and stinger guns and Five! Four! Three! Two! One! Attack!! Zombies, you are finished!"

But me and the ghosts had to squeeze our noses as tight as we could so we couldn't smell the zinger guns—which, P.S., smelled like a bathroom without air freshener. P-U!

Just then, a tornado came and 150 houses caught on fire at the same time. I was in trouble *big time*. So we started a war. We couldn't understand the zombies, though.

They said, "Arrrrrrahr."

I asked the ghosts what that was supposed to mean.

They said, "Brain juice."

Oh my gosh, the zombies wanted my brain! OK, that's common.

I was in big trouble—my mom woke up!!! I was embarrassed and scared. What if she thought they were friends of mine? But no, she was scared. I told her that ghosts are good. So she went back to bed. Phew.

The zombies got no brain juice—we ate them first. The ghosts made zombies on rye. I didn't take any chances.

You Shine Like Aphrodite

BY Michael A. Collazo, *Grade 3*

FROM *Abrazos de Mariposas / Butterfly Hugs*

20   Dear Mom,

I love you Mom.
Thank you for everything you have given me
You shine like Aphrodite (goddess of love and beauty)
Because you are loving and beautiful
I wish I could count how many hugs you give me
You are the number-one mom in the whole wide world
I hope you love me too
You are like a butterfly flying to the sky as an angel and
bird
In the evening you shine like the horizon
You are like a ladybug that solves problems as a finance
agent

Who Wants Love?

BY Quinn Wells, *Grade 4*

FROM *When the Carnival Is Closed, Winter 2011*

LOVE IS A GREAT THING because it's made out of hearts and beauty and prettiness and handsomeness and awesomeness. And POW!

Love goes slow. Love is ridiculous. Love is fast like a pony with a wizard costume on and a green mustache. Love is sad. Love is crazy. Love is around the world. Love is a deck of cards. Family Love is happy and cool. Boyfriend and girl-friend love is yuck and nasty.

When it comes to love, a man has to have a job, a good diploma, and has to have an eight-pack. And he has to cook and has to look handsome. He probably has to be in his 30s.

What To Do When You Meet An Alien

BY Laszlo Jentes Kuruna, *Grade 3*
FROM *Space Exploration for Beginners, Summer 2010*

22 Step 1: Ask if they have Harry Potter #3.

Step 2: If they have it, ask if you can borrow it.

Step 3: Watch it (with the alien, of course).

Step 4: Don't forget the popcorn with butter*.

Step 5: Make sure there are no meteor showers. (If there are, don't go outside.)

Step 6: If the alien's ship is broken, help it fix it.

Step 7: Drive the alien's spaceship to the airport in your truck.

Step 8: Launch the spaceship off your truck. Make sure your truck is on fire.

Step 9: Call the fire department.

Step 10: Shoot yourself out of a cannon and follow the alien.

Step 11: Go to its home planet and stay for a year.

Step 12: Go home.

* *Alien butter.*

What to Do at a Fancy Dinner

BY Renata Dagley, *Grade 6*
FROM *BLAM! You're There, Spring 2011*

LIKE ME, you might be invited to a fancy-shmancy dinner by your best friend. A fancy-shmancy dinner is when a bunch of older people go eat expensive food. They also wear black suits for men and dresses with pearl necklaces and white gloves for the ladies. Now, we all want to look extravagant, not like a girl or boy who has no manners whatsoever. Here are some ways to be fancy! I mean, hey, they worked for me!

1. Smile every single second. If you don't smile, everyone will think you're bored or don't like the food. They'll definitely be offended.

2. Tutus make everything better. Everybody at the dinner will be wearing them!

3. Ask many questions to the servers. They looove questions. Example: "Does this have any sugar? Will I get sick if I eat this too fast? Wanna play tag?" Speaking of tag...

4. When you think the old people get annoying or boring, ask them if they want to run laps around the building. Keep everyone active!

5. Be sure to spit your food out if you don't like it. Chefs like to know if you don't enjoy your food!

Well, if you use all these steps, then you probably... Wait. Now that I think about it, when I did any of these things I got yelled at! Oh well, bye!

What Do You Really Want?

by Yerika Reyes, Grade 10

What do you answer when someone asks you what you want?

Love?

                    Money?

                                    A Genie?

More wishes?

                A better planet?

                                  HEALTH?

Less Poverty?

                World Peace?

ACCEPTANCE INTO YOUR COLLEGE OF CHOICE?

                                    Fame?

                To End World Hunger?

Longer Hair?

Straight hair?

A cure for cancer?

A donor?

Fairness?

Equality?

How vain or serious are your deepest wishes?

What do you really want when the door is shut?
When no one is looking,
while you lay in bed,
with your eyes shut.

What desires go through your mind?

How DEEP or SHALLOW do your waters run?

~~~~~

What do *I* really want?

When *I* shut the door,
lie in bed alone.
With *my* eyes closed I want...

I want it all.

Mostly though,
I want to be heard.

I want to know that my voice counts
that people are listening.

What *I* really want...

I want to write and be known.
Not praised but **UNDERSTOOD**.

What Happened

BY Sophie Ljung, *Grade 3*
FROM *Zombies Can't Write, But Kids Can!, Spring 2010*

ZOMBIES CAN'T KISS, and everybody knows that. But yesterday, the weirdest thing happened.

You see, taking out trash is my job. I'm a trashman. So, one night, at precisely 12:09 am, I went to take out the trash. Naturally, I went in alleys collecting garbage. But, when I got to 32nd Street, I saw this weird blue man with another woman just like him. I figured it was a zombie species, the most feared. I got a closer look, and they both leaned in and ...well, I don't have to tell you everything.

We Meet Again

BY The Students of Mr. Pérez's Class, *Grade 6*
FROM *New Calmeca Academy of Fine Arts and Dual Language,*
Spring 2011

ONCE UPON A TIME there was an old man named Grampa Grump. Grampa Grump lived in a trashcan in an alley in Chicago. It was a dirty alley, with lots of rats running around. Grampa Grump lived in the alley because he didn't like to see people. Grampa Grump was a nickname kids in the neighborhood gave him because they didn't know his real name. His real name was James. He wore a broken old hat, cracked glasses, and dirty clothes. He tried to keep his clothes clean but it was hard when he lived in a trashcan.

James really liked hanging out with people, but ever since he was born, he always brought bad luck to anybody he cared about. When he was a little boy, his friends would always fall off their bikes or trip over him. His parents had bad luck with jobs and rent, until he grew up and moved out.

When he was older he met a woman and married her, and for a while they had good luck. They had a little girl named Jennifer and were very happy. After a while, though, James's bad luck started coming back, and he decided that the best thing would be to go away so he couldn't bring bad luck to his family. James never got to see his daughter grow up but he knew that he couldn't keep bringing bad luck to his family. He moved into an alley and everyone started calling him Grampa Grump. He stayed in the alley for 20 years, and his daughter grew up and had a son of her own.

One gray, cloudy day, a little boy named Jimmy was playing with some friends. Jimmy was a friendly boy, who always wanted to talk to people. Jimmy was seven, and he loved playing outside with his friends. He was tall and wore glasses and a baseball cap all the time. Jimmy and his friends were walking down the street and saw a dark, scary-looking alley.

"Grampa Grump lives down there," said one of Jimmy's friends, who was called Eric.

"Who is that?" asked Jimmy.

"He's a really nice, friendly guy," said Johnny, another friend, who liked to play jokes on Jimmy.

"I dare you to go down there and say hi to Grampa Grump," said Eric.

"Sure, if you say he's a really nice guy," said Jimmy, who was very friendly and trusting.

So Jimmy started walking down the alley, but he was a little nervous because it was dark and he couldn't see much. It was foggy and cold in the alley, and he could hear rats scratching around in the dark. But Jimmy kept going, because he never went back on a dare.

At the end of the alley, Jimmy saw a trashcan. He knocked on top of the trashcan and called, "Hello?"

"What do you want?" growled a voice from the trashcan.

"I'd like to be your friend," said Jimmy, even though he was nervous. Just then, Grampa Grump poked his head over the edge of the trashcan. "I don't want to be anyone's friend. Go away," he yelled at Jimmy. Jimmy was sad because he also liked making new friends.

"No, I want to stay and be your friend," he continued. This made Grampa Grump angry, and he jumped out of the trashcan and started chasing Jimmy back down the alley. Jimmy ran very fast back to his friends, but when he got out of the alley, his friends weren't there. They knew Grampa Grump would be angry and they had run away. Jimmy was alone and scared. He decided to run home. Grampa Grump was so mad that Jimmy had disturbed him that he chased Jimmy all the way home.

When Jimmy got home he shouted "Mom! There's a crazy man following me!" Jimmy's mom opened the door and Jimmy ran inside. She went outside to stop Grampa Grump and shouted, "Stop chasing my son! Who are you?" She stood in front of Grampa Grump, and he looked at her and said, "Jennifer? Is that you?"

Jimmy's mom stared at him, and whispered "Dad?" She realized that Grampa Grump was her own father who had left 20 years ago.

"Yes, it's me. I'm sorry I left you so long ago. I was worried that I was going to bring you bad luck, because that always happens to people I care about," said Grampa Grump. Jimmy's mom was sad about this, but she was also happy to see her father again, who was Jimmy's grandfather, and the man Jimmy had been named after. He was smiling for the first time in 20 years. Just then, the clouds drifted away, and the sun started shining.

"What good luck!" exclaimed Jimmy's mom, and Grampa Grump realized that he could bring good luck as well as bad, and that he just needed to have a positive attitude. All his life he had been negative, and it caused bad luck. From that moment on, Grampa Grump was happy and positive and brought good luck to Jimmy and his whole family.

A Valentine's Poem

BY Brennan Klaassen, *Grade 7*

FROM *When the Carnival Is Closed, Winter 2011*

Roses are blue.
Violets are red.
The poem is messed up
just like my friend Ned.

He wakes up in the morning
and forgets to shower—
when he gets to school,
his BO's got power.

I have a horrible smell now
up my nose,
and when I am offered cologne,
anything goes.

The Untold Romance of Nancy Pantsy and Brock the Rock

BY The Students of Ms. Novak's Class, *Grade 12*

FROM *John Hope College Prep High School, Winter 2011*

OUTSIDE UNITED HIGH, there was a statue of a very manly, muscular unicorn. United was just off the intersection of I Have a Dream Highway and the Pathway to Success. The statue of the unicorn was rearing up, as if suspended in the middle of a wild gallop. The unicorn was made of grayish-blue stone and covered in moss. The unicorn was the school mascot, and he represented the United Unicorns, which had been a wonderful football team until the day their quarterback Brock disappeared.

Brock had disappeared almost three years earlier. Unbeknownst to the students, Brock was actually under an evil spell cast on him by the Principal of United, Barry the Unmarried. Barry had been very jealous of Brock, the handsome, intelligent, and popular quarterback of the football team. Barry was jealous because when he was in high

34

school he was a very awkward, socially inept, unpopular member of the chess team. Barry had played cricket and been on the math team as well, but he was never very successful at either activity. So Barry the Unmarried, in a jealous rage, waited and watched from the window of his office until Brock, the most dedicated of the football players, was leaving football practice. Then Barry used his evil wand to turn Brock into the stone unicorn in front of the school.

Brock could see and hear but he couldn't move or talk or scream for help. For three lonely, miserable years, Brock had been trapped in the form of a stone unicorn. Luckily the weather at the intersection of I Have a Dream Highway and the Pathway to Success was always sunny and beautiful, so at least Brock was never rained or snowed on.

In this particular year, the co-captain of the cheerleading team was named Nancy Chula Pantsy. She had indigo skin and teal hair, and was very beautiful. She had always felt second-best to her rival, the captain of the cheerleading team. The captain was named Elise the Beast, and she had a lot of curly, fuchsia hair and always wore sequins. Elise and Nancy had been practicing for the school-wide talent show. Nancy had made up a wonderful dance for the event, and taught it to the rest of the squad. It was called the Jumping Jack. While they were practicing, some teachers and Barry the Unmarried came to watch. They were amazed.

Barry cried out, "Who made up this wonderful dance? I want to give an award to whoever made up this! I will give a magical homework elf for one week to the choreographer."

"I did it, Mr. Unmarried," Elise declared, stealing the credit that Nancy was due.

Nancy was too sweet to call Elise a liar, or tell the principal what had really happened, but she was devastated. Not knowing what else to do, she stormed out of the school and sat down next to Brock the stone unicorn. She started venting out loud about Elise the Beast to Brock. Brock had secretly watched Nancy come and go from school, cheerleading practice, and choir practice. He had heard her singing, and she had an angelic voice. Brock was smitten with Nancy.

"I can't believe Elise the Beast stole the credit for the dance, and the homework elf! I am sick of playing second fiddle to her!" Nancy fumed, looking up at Brock for understanding.

Even though he knew he wouldn't be heard, Brock said, "Oh, Nancy, I see how great you are."

Nancy leapt back in shock, because she had heard this in a soft, deep, baritone.

"Did you say something?" Nancy said to the unicorn. Then she said to herself, "This is crazy. That unicorn did not just say something to me."

Just then, Nancy's mom pulled up in front of the school in the family hovercraft, and Nancy hopped in to go home.

Every day for the next month while waiting for her mom to pick her up, Nancy told her deepest secrets to Brock the unicorn.

"I feel like you're the only one who really understands me," Nancy said to him. "Maybe it makes me crazy that I can hear you talking back to me, but I love our conversations."

"You're the only one in three years who has heard me," Brock said sweetly. By the end of the month, Brock decided to tell Nancy that Barry the Unmarried had cast an evil spell on him, and that he was secretly the missing quarterback. Nancy had come to the school after the enchantment, and didn't remember Brock in human form, but she'd heard the stories of the missing football player. She listened in shocked amazement.

"How can we break the evil spell?" she asked.

"Well," said Brock, "I know from listening over the years that Elise the Beast and Barry the Unmarried are in cahoots. And I know that Barry cast this spell on me out of jealousy. I also know that Elise is very jealous of your lovely voice and sweet personality, and silky teal hair. She plans to turn you into a stone bench before prom night if we don't break the spell, so moss will grow on you, and everyone will sit on you."

"That's awful," Nancy cried. "What will break the spell?"

"Go snoop in Barry's office, and see if you can find his wand, or any clues to see how I can get out of this pickle," said Brock.

Nancy went late at night and climbed into Barry's office window. She started going through the drawers of his desk. She found books of spells, false teeth, several jars of earwax, and a list of students that had been turned into homework elves. Nancy didn't find a wand, and as she was fleeing the school and running toward Brock, she ran into Elise the Beast.

"What are you doing?" Elise demanded.

Nancy ignored Elise and threw her arms around Brock. She started crying, and said, "I'm so sorry I can't help you! But I love you!"

Suddenly the stone unicorn shattered, and there was Brock in his United Unicorns football uniform. Nancy was amazed to see that the spell was broken, because neither of them had known that the spell would be broken if Brock found true love before what would have been his senior prom. As soon as the curse on Brock was broken, all of the homework elves were turned back into their old human selves.

Even though Brock and Nancy were too nice to wish for revenge, the curse was magically reversed, and Barry the Unmarried was turned into a muscular, moss-covered stone unicorn. Elise was turned into a stone bench, next to the unicorn. When prom came a week later, the students of United sat on the bench for photographs, and Brock and Nancy were the best-looking couple in attendance. They lived happily ever after.

But before they lived happily ever after, they danced the night away at prom. Nancy led everyone in the Jumping Jack, and everyone realized that she was the one who had made it up. No one even noticed that Elise the Beast was missing.

Tornado of Memories

BY Klea Kahari, *Grade 7*
FROM *Solomon School, Fall 2010*

ONCE UPON A TIME, there was a peaceful, beautiful town
named Memoryville. In this town, everyone threw away
their memories, which were replaced by others, and this is
how the cycle continued. No one knew exactly where the
memories went. Most of them didn't care. All of the resi-
dents just plucked the memories out of their brains and
threw them into the air. When thrown, the memories were
never remembered again.

At the Ceremony of Memories everyone was to throw
away all of their memories, cherished or cursed. On this day,
something was not right. One little girl named Klea Kahari
had not wanted to throw away her most prized memory of
her father, who had passed away four months ago, feeding
the baby ducks in the pond nearby her house. This was the
first time Klea really felt affection, because all of her other

memories were forced away from her every ceremony. Since her father died, she had been holding on to her feeling and her mother sensed it. "Klea, I can sense that you are holding onto a memory. You still have an hour until the ceremony ends at midnight."

"I don't want to forget Dad, though! I know you have already and that is what the memory is about! I will always remember Dad, no matter what ceremonies come along to say otherwise."

"I haven't forgotten him, either. I've always kept him in my heart. If this memory really means a lot to you, you can keep it. But we must not tell anyone. If anyone does find out, we will most likely be arrested. I know there is no point of throwing away memories, but keep it on the down low, okay?"

All of the good memories, which all went to the same place that no one knew about, the abandoned hut by the river, each had minds of their own. They thought how nice it was for someone to actually be happy in this community, after seeing Klea's joy from memory. These good memories all gathered together, creating a giant tornado—a tornado of memories. The tornado swarmed over Memoryville, filling the people's heads with the long-forgotten memories that brought them joy. The people of Memoryville thought, "Remembering memories is not so bad, and it doesn't burn brain cells like we thought."

Memoryville banned the act of memory forgetting. Klea Kahari was found by the mayor of Memoryville,

Mayor Memory, and was thanked. A statue of Klea was placed in the center of the town. She became the new mayor of Memoryville and would be praised for as long as Memoryville stood. This is how the act of remembering came to be.

Time to Jump

BY Alexandra Leiseca, *Grade 5*
FROM *Middle School Writing Camp, Summer 2011*

NATALIE BROWN WAS 12 YEARS OLD and lived in Hovingham, England. Her parents, Dead Thorn Brown and Sickly Sweet Brown, were the worst parents anyone could imagine. Dead Thorn was a walrus of a man with a huge beard. He looked remarkably like Santa Claus. He wore a near black tuxedo except at parties when he wore "extremely fancy" clothes— he thought the tuxedo was too casual for that. He was very rich and snotty. Sickly Sweet was a slightly chubby woman with ever-so-neat hair that was always either flat-ironed or curled. She always wore long, skin-tight dresses. She could be mistaken for an overgrown mushroom. They lived in a mansion in the country.

Natalie was an extremely pretty 12 year old girl. She had light brown hair with golden highlights. Her wavy hair often bounced on her shoulders as she ran. Her eyes matched the color of her hair.

Dead Thorn and Sickly Sweet were not Natalie's real parents. Her real parents were separated from her when she was very young. Now, 12 years later, Natalie looked out her bedroom window and wished she was back with her real family and away from the extremely mean Browns. They expected her to be proper and perfect—in other words, just like them. But Natalie was more crazy and carefree. She would have liked to hang out and read fantasy and science fiction books or run into the nearby forest to play by herself but the Browns, as she called them, would rather she played piano.

Natalie was bored with the morning routine which usually included having breakfast on china and crystal in the big, formal dining room, going upstairs and getting dressed in the jeans that she liked, and then having to change into the itchy dresses and stockings that the Browns made her wear, and then waiting for the maid to come in and wash the already-clean windows promptly at 9:35 AM. The maid was a nice lady who knew that the Browns would get furious if she came in even one minute early or late so sometimes she would wait outside in the vast courtyard until the exact second the clock turned to 9:35 AM.

One particular morning, on a particularly bad day, Natalie heard the doors open to the entrance hall, signaling that the maid had come in. Knowing that she would vacuum all morning, Natalie stomped upstairs, disgusted with

43

the dress she had to wear that day—ugly purple with flowers the disturbing pink color of medicine she had to take when she was sick. Natalie walked into her princess-like room, with thick formal tapestries she didn't approve of, and went to the window.

She began watching the birds while the sunlight was still fresh and soft. As she watched them, Natalie noticed the way the birds rarely ever traveled by themselves, freely. She realized how different she was from the birds. Natalie felt like she was always controlled and trapped by a life that restricted her from doing the things that she truly liked. She felt like she had her own little bird in her body, trying to break free from her limited shell. She wanted more than ever to be with her true family, people she thought would let her express her feelings, and also understand them.

Then, out of nowhere, a crazy idea popped into her head! She would jump out of the window and find her real family!

Natalie opened the window and climbed into it. She would jump out on the count of three.

One... two... SMACK!

Natalie jumped back. A golden piece of paper had drifted into her face, startling her. The paper read, *Luck will come to you in three ways.* Not knowing what this meant, Natalie balled it up and threw it away.

Okay, she thought. *Time to jump.*

And she did. The air whipped her face and hair as she fell to the ground. Fear gripped her insides and pulled them.

She was only a couple feet away from the ground now. "I'm going to die!" Natalie thought.

Just one inch...

She squeezed her eyes shut. Then, she felt a soaring sensation. She was flying!

The Time I Lost Half of My Heart

BY Christopher Dampier, *Grade 8*
FROM *Harvard School of Excellence, Fall 2010*

46   IT WAS NOVEMBER 14, 2009, the day my grandfather died. I was coming home from my little cousin's birthday party when I saw the ambulance parked in front of my house. I was standing outside while my cousin, Bre, ran into the house.

All of a sudden I saw my mom running toward me. She threw her arms around me and I saw that she was crying. Then I saw a white body bag being pulled from the house. When I saw the body bag I was sad, but happy at the same time because I knew my grandfather didn't have to go through any more pain.

When his heart stopped, I felt my heart stopped, too, but my heart had to keep beating even though he was out of my life. I started to think that I had nothing else, but then I opened my eyes and saw my mother and grandmother.

That's when I started thinking that I had to go to school and do what I needed to do.

When I was down, my grandfather would always help me pick my head up. He told me to never give up on anything, because life is too short to be playing all the time. He told me to live life like it was my last day on earth.

When I realized that he was gone I did not want to waste any more of my life. So I wanted to do better in school and do my best to join the NBA. When he passed, I told myself I wanted to do this so that I could take care of my family. I wanted to show him that I could do better than what other people expect of me.

I decided I would do better by going to school more often. I would get better grades by doing all my homework and projects. I also wanted to go to the NBA so that is why I joined the basketball team. I now try my best in school and at practice. I even started going to after-school to get help with my homework and projects.

I can still remember when my granddad, my mother, and I cooked together for his 73rd birthday. It was so fun. We were all having fun and he was smiling. I will never forget that moment. I remember the smell of his Old Spice cologne, which was his favorite.

I still have his fishing pole that he always had with him. The last thing he said to me was, "Turn off the fan."

I still remember so much about him. I can remember his shouting. When he shouted everyone would be scared, but usually all he wanted was a glass of ice water.

47

I can remember when the funeral happened. I was sad because I couldn't see him anymore, but happy that he wouldn't feel any more pain.

48

The Thriller

BY Marvin Galvan, *Grade 5*
FROM *BLAM! You're There, Spring 2011*

THERE WAS A DOCTOR in a restaurant eating sushi.

As he was eating, he saw a werewolf outside crossing the street and said, "OMG!"

The doctor ran, but the werewolf caught up to him at the gasoline station and the werewolf ate the doctor. Werewolves love eating doctors because their brains are really juicy.

The werewolf doctor started dancing. He heard music in the restaurant. He started dancing the "Thriller" dance from Michael Jackson. Zombies came to join them and people on the street were scared, but then the people joined the dance and they had a great time. Suddenly, Michael Jackson woke up from his graveyard and started the Thriller dance.

The werewolf-eating doctor and Michael Jackson started to dance together.

"I like your moves," Michael Jackson said to the werewolf doctor.

The werewolf howled, "Thank you."

The Things You Do When Nobody Is Watching

BY Robin Xu, *Grade 11*

FROM *Young Writers Camp with Local Authors, Summer 2010*

YOU SUCK YOUR THUMB. Not a lot, just a little, so nobody will 51
make fun of you and say, "Aw, look at the baby. You must be
lost. Don't you know where you are, baby? This is first grade.
Go back to preschool, you dumb baby." You do it even though
your mother says it will give you a lisp and buck teeth.

You throw the popsicle stick on the lawn when you're
done. You don't even want to go inside for a second to toss it
in the garbage can. Besides, wood is from trees, and trees are
like grass. But after a few minutes you feel guilty and bury
it in the flower garden instead, deep under the soil, where it
will be able to grow.

You pick your nose. There's a certain way to go about it.
First, you look around to make sure that the boy you like
isn't nearby. Then you rub your nose while staring off into
the distance, pretending to think about absolutely nothing.

If you catch someone looking, your last hope is to pretend to sneeze. It's an art, even if you're pretty sure each time that everyone can see right through your plan.

You make a Father's Day card for your father. Every year in May, you make a Mother's Day card at school. You draw flowers and write poems and paste sequins. By the time Father's Day comes around, school has let out and most children have long forgotten. But you see the pink card on the fireplace mantle and feel guilty. Your father puts his green one next to it.

You do things you shouldn't. You don't get caught, so you do them again.

You count the seats between you and the most popular girl in your class so that you'll end up sitting next to each other when the teacher assigns new tables. You know this girl. You've always known her. This girl has the most Barbies, the bike with the pink streamers, the first cell phone, the first iPod, a high school boyfriend, AND tickets to the Twilight midnight premiere meet-and-greet. You'd die before admitting that you wish you were friends with her. But maybe if you were, you could date a high school boy, too. Maybe you'd even get to touch Edward Cullen.

You make up stories because your real life isn't exciting enough, but you rarely find opportunities to share them because most people you talk to already know the truth about you.

You stand in the mirror with a hairbrush and pretend you're in a music video for your favorite song. Easy if your favorite song is by Taylor Swift, slightly harder if it's by Lady Gaga. If you're a 90s child, you tied your shirt up into a crop top and belted "Oops! I Did It Again." If you're a little older, maybe Blondie is more appropriate.

You cry. You've stopped being upset around your parents because they'll inevitably ask what's wrong. As parents, it has always been their job to be overly nosy about every aspect of your life, but you just don't feel like talking to them anymore.

You read romance novels. You don't know that the authors of those novels are catering to your specific demographic, and you eat up their every word.

You tweeze your eyebrows for the first time. You get distracted thinking of names for your future children that would go well with your crush's last name, so they come out slightly crooked. You hold your breath when you come downstairs for dinner, but nobody comments on them.

You try to find good hiding places for the new "grownup" underwear you bought at Victoria's Secret when you went to the mall with your friends. You're not sure what you bought it for, or even how to wear it exactly, but what you do know is that your mother wouldn't approve. You finally hide it in the very back of your bottom drawer next to your stash of disposable razors and lip gloss behind the stacks and stacks of colored capris from Old Navy that you hate. "Mom, nobody wears capris anymore. And nobody wears matching tracksuits either. God, you'd might as well ask me to wear tie-dye and metallic rainboots or something. No, Mom, I was kidding! Fine, buy the capris, but you're just wasting

53

your money. I won't wear them." And you don't. But somehow, you don't end up wearing your grownup underwear either.

You write. And write. And write. You start off with characters borrowed from *Sisterhood of the Traveling Pants*, but slowly your writing gets better.

You do things you shouldn't, but this time, you do get caught. You realize that your mother knows a lot more about what you do than you thought, but it's not because you're bad at hiding. You realize that she normally lets all these things slide. So when she chooses to catch you, you realize that it must be important.

You get things done. You call State Farm to quote car insurance and pick up Raisin Bran on the way home. You scrub the bathtub (but don't tell anyone). Nobody notices, but you do it again the next week.

You try on your prom dress not once, not twice, but 14 times before the big night. You have to make sure it goes with your shoes. And your purse. And your nails. And your makeup. And your hair. And your date.

You sneak into your parents' bedroom at 3 am after finally finishing your AP Lang essay. They're already sleeping; you're now the first one in the house to get up in the morning and the last to go to bed at night. You kiss them goodnight for the first time in years because next year at college you will no longer be able to.

Somewhere along the way, you grow up.

She Is My Heart

BY Ronald Uruchimo, *Grade 3*
FROM *Abrazos de Mariposas/Butterfly Hugs*

My mom is beautiful like a pony
She is pink and nice like a flower
She loves butterflies
My mom is a bright star
My mom likes plants
She's a princess
She loves pets
My mom loves the sky
She loves me and I love her
She is a heart
She is my heart
She loves dogs
She is the best mom ever
She loves outside where the sun is shining

My mom loves her room
And she loves to make cupcakes
And she loves pie
I love you, Mom!

Shakespeare: A Compilation

BY Matthew Schumm, *Grade 9*

FROM *Young Writers Camp with Local Authors, Summer 2011*

A KING NAMED LEAR DIES. 57

His son, Hamlet, descends, into madness and falls in
love with a really annoying feminist named
Katherina, who runs off and meets a
Fairy that turns Athenian worker-actors into donkeys.

She bakes one of them into a blood pie, along with two
guys named Chiron and Demetrius. Emperor Lucius then
sentences her to slow death by thirst.

She becomes a witch, escapes using her newfound
powers, and tells a guy named Macbeth he'll become king.
Macbeth kills the current king and ascends to the throne.
His army abhors him though so...

They slack off and take a trip to a place called Messina.
In the army is a soldier named Claudio who gets angry a lot

and a soldier named Benedick who makes jokes. Much is soon ado about nothing.

King Macbeth is then usurped by his brother, Frederick, whose daughter, Rosalind, falls in love with an awesome wrestler named Orlando.

Macbeth flees to an island, where he meets a spirit called Ariel and a mooncalf called Caliban. Then a ship wrecks on the island, with two sailors still alive.

They explain that they each have an identical twin, and they went missing in the shipwreck.

One of the two shipwrecked sailors is named Romeo, and he falls in love with Macbeth's daughter, Juliet. However, Macbeth forbids the two from seeing each other ever again.

Meanwhile, Romeo's shipwrecked identical twin sister Viola lands in Ilyria and fakes being a man to get into King Leontes's court. He discovers her, though, and marries her.

Years later, they are happily married, but Leontes begins to suspect her of adultery, and exiles her.

She then captures the heart of two men who compete in a tournament to win her hand in marriage.

The two gentlemen are from Verona, named Valentine and Proteus, and it turns out Proteus is already married to a woman named Julia. So Viola marries Valentine, and they have a son named Caius Martius, who becomes a general in the Roman army. However, he is killed when he betrays the Romans.

His distant descendant, Julius Caesar, is also assassinated when Roman senators suspect him of trying to take over.

Then, a Roman noble and friend of Caesar's named Mark Antony falls in love with a woman named Cleopatra, but ends up losing a promotion because of it. He gets angry and tricks a guy named Othello into murdering his own wife, Desdemona. Mark Antony is discharged from the Roman army and fined, but he makes his way to Windsor, England under the alias of John Falstaff and decides to court two affluent women named Mistress Ford and Mistress Page for their money.

However, he cannot marry either of them unless he can answer a riddle thought up by their dad, Antiochus.

Luckily, a duke disguised as a friar helps him figure out the answer to the riddle, and Mark Antony marries Mistress Page.

Against the wishes of her father, Mistress Ford elopes with a man named Imogen. They seek shelter in the castle of the

King of Navarre, who took an oath not to seek out the company of women for three years.

When a woman named Cressida visits, the King falls in love with her, and kills a man named Diomedes who tries to woo her for himself.

He then renounces all his earthly possessions.

His servant Antonio, a kind, friendly man, leaves his boss and becomes a merchant in Venice.

He then reluctantly marries a woman named Helena, and all's well that ends well.

·

The Secret Agent Lisa Jackson and the Hunt for the Secret Sidekick

BY The Students of Ms. Pendley's Class, *Grade 3*

FROM *Dodge Renaissance Academy, Winter 2011*

AGENT LISA JACKSON was not an ordinary agent with the CIS. In her black coat, black hat, glasses and utility belt, she had the ability to keep an eye on the worst criminals in the country: grass-eating fish. In her hat, she had a magnifying glass that allowed her to both find clues and find prints of the grass-eating fish. Lisa's sidekick, who also worked for the CIS, was a chicken named Destiny. Destiny was a master of karate and had glasses that could see through walls. She also had the ability to call for backup by laying signal eggs and she could see the enemy's plan by laying psychic eggs.

One day, Agent Lisa Jackson got a call from her boss. "Agent Jackson, I have a special mission for you. Elmer, the notorious grass-eating fish, is safely in a maximum-security prison. It's guarded with nets and sharks. However, our intelligence tells us that Elmer's secret sidekick is going to try and break him out. Your mission is to find out the side-kick's name and discover his plan."

Agent Lisa Jackson and Destiny went to their number-one source for information on grass-eating fish: the grass-eating fish master. The grass-eating fish master was named Derek Foster. He had a brown Mohawk and made a mean cup of coffee. He told the agents, "I don't know what you're talking about. I don't know anything. But if I did know something, I would say 'go to a log cabin in the middle of the secret desert to find what you're looking for.'"

To get to the log cabin, they went to the gadget master at the CIS, Ms. Pendley, and asked for a super-secret skateboard that went 2,000 miles an hour. Ms. Pendley said, "I can give you this skateboard, but there's something you should know about it. It can easily catch on fire, so you need to be careful with it in the desert." So Secret Agent Lisa Jackson and Destiny took the skateboard to the log cabin in the desert. The cabin was guarded by ninjas.

Destiny stepped forward and said, "Mamute, we meet again." The leader of the ninja guards stepped forward and said, "You just woke the dragon up. Prepare for pain."

While Destiny and Mamute entered into their non-fatal karate battle, Secret Agent Lisa Jackson took the skateboard and zoomed straight past the battle into the front door of the log cabin.

Who will Agent Jackson find inside the cabin? Will Destiny defeat the ninjas? Does that skateboard come with a warranty? Crack the case and write the ending!

Rescuing BlaBoom

BY Jennifer Resendiz, *Grade 5*
FROM *BLAM! You're There, Spring 2011*

ONCE UPON A MEDIEVAL TIME there lived a mad scientist called 63
BlaBoom Sweethearts. He was tough but girly. People said
he graduated from DePaul University but no one believed
he was even accepted since he was so abnormal. One day he
was in his secret lair when he invented "The Orange" and
along with that "The Fork." Then, the mad scientist got man-
napped. It was a mystery—no one knew how it happened.
(The orange sometimes thinks it was his grandmother but
the fork slaps him.)

At 6 pm, stuck inside a room filled with liquids, the odd
orange and the fork started to talk.

"Hey fork, hey fork, hey fork."

"*WHAT?!*"

The orange was very irritating. "Heeelloooo?! My name is—ahem—the Irritating Orange," the irritating orange told the fork.

"Uhh, duhh. It's very obvious that you are very irritating and an orange."

"Oh, well. Hey fork?" the irritating orange said.

"Yeah, my name is Fork. Just because it was my parents' decision—but I would like my name to be *metal!*"

The irritating Orange thought the fork was the irritating one because all he talked about was that the spoon broke up with him and how he loved metal.

After a while, the orange and the fork both thought of rescuing BlaBoom. Since they were in a room alone, they got really bored and the orange finally thought of something fun to do. "Let's go and save BlaBoom," said the Irritating Orange.

"Okay, but first tell me—why do you think the spoon broke up with me?" Fork asked, as if he was very innocent.

The orange looked inside his smartphone and accessed his apps. "I have found BlaBoom with my smartphone. We shall go!"

They dressed up in black and went to rescue BlaBoom.

When the Irritating Orange and the fork were walking with their little feet to find and rescue BlaBoom, the fork slipped on a banana peel. Orange, with a piece of banana in his mouth and the other half in his hand said, "Oh, sorry.

I got a little hungry with too much action going on." Poor Fork. He had fainted and was lying on the floor.

Moving on, they were walking when invisible ninjas popped out (well, that's what the irritating Orange said). The irritating Orange was fighting "the invisible ninjas." The two were victorious! They kept looking around the strange place where they had appeared. The fork felt as if he was in a horror movie. He also thought it was a lot like *Resident Evil*.

Bam! A noise startled them.

The fork jumped on top of the orange thinking it had hands to hold him up. He immediately slipped down the orange and fell onto the floor.

They were walking down a strange hall with mirrors all over. The fork heard someone playing Bob Dylan on the guitar. Fork looked closely and saw it was the orange.

"Sorry, I get excited at these moments in a story," said the orange.

Then a clown popped out and they took off his mask. Orange and Fork were hugging in fear.

It was BlaBoom in the clown mask!

The Presentation

BY Lucie McKnight, *Grade 7*
FROM *Middle School Writing Extravaganza, Summer 2011*

SALLY WOKE UP to the sound of the birds singing and the sight of the Wyoming mountains outside of her window. She pulled the blankets off of her and started heading downstairs to cut holes in a fresh paper bag so she could go to work.

Sally went into the kitchen and found the key to the drawer where she kept the previous paper bags. She put the key in the lock and opened the drawer. Instead of seeing the reassuring soft, papery brown of the paper bags, all Sally saw was the harsh green interior of the drawer. This could not be happening; Sally couldn't possibly go outside without a fresh paper bag to hide her face from the world. The last time she had run out of paper bags was three years ago and she hadn't left her house for two months afterwards until the next paper bag delivery came.

Sally couldn't hide from the world forever though. In fact, she *had* to go to work today because of a presentation she had to give. If Sally didn't show up today, she would be fired. And she needed this job—it wasn't cheap to buy 365 paper bags a year.

Sally rushed into the living room and scrambled around for the phone. When she finally found it, she picked it up and speed-dialed the nearest grocery store. She nervously paced while the phone dialed. Then a friendly voice picked up.

"Hello, this is Foodville Grocery, how can I help you?"

"Hi, do you do deliveries?"

"Yes, ma'am, we do. What do you need delivered?"

"I need ten packs of small brown paper bags."

"Excuse me? Ten packs?"

"You heard me. Please get them here as fast as possible. Thank you!"

She slammed down the phone and ran upstairs to get dressed before the delivery came.

Sally put on her best jeans and a pink blouse because pink went well with the color brown of the generic bags. She wanted to look her best for her presentation to hopefully get a promotion from her boss.

Sally brushed her hair and teeth and went downstairs to wait for the delivery. While she was waiting, she picked up a travel novel to calm her down. Sally's secret was that she loved traveling books and learning about new places, but she couldn't travel outside her hometown with a paper bag on her head and it was unthinkable to take it off.

Currently, Sally was reading a particularly interesting travel book about boat tours down the Amazon River, but she was too nervous to read. She stood up and paced back and forth while she waited. And waited, and waited. Time seemed to be moving slower than usual and Sally was worried that she was going to miss her presentation.

Finally, Sally's phone rang. She ran to answer the phone.

"Hello?" she said frantically.

"Sally? Is that you? Where are you?" It was her boss.

"I'm at home," she replied with as much calmness as she could muster.

"Why? Do you have any recollection of the *extremely* important presentation you were supposed to give in 15 minutes?"

"I'm sorry! I ran out of paper bags!" she said in a slightly hushed tone.

"Oh, really, Sally? Is that necessary?" her boss replied, angry.

"Yes! I can't—"

Just as she was starting to reply, she was interrupted by a harsh three knocks at the door. She ended the call, slammed down the phone and ran for the door. She quickly put her eye up to the peek hole and confirmed it was the deliveryman by looking at the large box of packages of paper bags.

Sally stepped behind the door so the deliveryman wouldn't see her and opened the door.

"Umm, is anyone home?" the deliveryman asked, confused. Sally stuck her arm out and grabbed the box, closed the door and shoved the money out the mail slot.

Sally ran to the kitchen, grabbed the scissors, and sloppily cut out two uneven holes. She grabbed all of her papers and materials she needed for her presentation and ran out the door.

She sprinted down the pathway to her house and onto the main road. Sally looked in front and saw her bus inches away from the stop. Sally ran as fast as she possibly could. Suddenly, the wind picked up, not only blowing her papers away from her, but knocking the bag off of her head too.

Sally immediately put her hands over her face as an impulse. She hadn't shown her face to another human in 12 years. She felt like everyone was staring as she got on the bus, and her face was as red as a tomato out of embarrassment.

When Sally arrived at work, she tried to draw as little attention to herself as possible. She felt like everyone in the whole office could hear every single footstep. She finally reached the bland hallway leading to the office where she would give her presentation. The walk down the hallway was the longest walk she ever took. Sally opened the door and everyone gasped.

Poem of a Poem

BY Phillip Ramey, *Grade 6*

FROM *BLAM! You're There, Spring 2011*

70

A poem—
Is it true
or false
a trick question
like do stairs
go up or down
why can't I answer
a poem it is
confusing if
DaVinci can be
an artist
can I be a poemist?
but when
you think
this poem

may be
true or
false
could it be
both?

71

A Place Above Your Head

BY Cyrus LeMoine, *Grade 4*

FROM *I Need Everyone to See My Sparkles, Winter 2010*

THERE IS A PLACE above your head. It is invisible—unless you can shoot lasers out of your eyes, like me. If you could see it, it would look like an upside down mountain or an earth node. It represents your mood. The people in this world act out your mood. If you are angry, they are angry and battle each other. If you are happy, they are happy and shake hands and eat three scoops of your favorite ice cream. (Unless you don't like ice cream. Then they eat carrots.) If you are sad, they cry and mope around and eat over-boiled spinach. They look exactly like you.

The buildings they live in are three-story brick houses. The houses also act your mood. If you are angry, the houses scowl and their windows break. If you are happy, the houses smile and are in perfect condition. If you are sad, the buildings frown and the plumbing leaks. The weather shows your moods, too. If you are happy, it's sunny. If you are sad, it rains. If you are angry, there is a thunderstorm with a pulsing *boom*.

If you fight someone, the places crash together and the people above your head fight each other. Every day, they eat every single thing on the food triangle. They eat hot dogs how you like to for lunch, but they are usually very healthy. They speak Gobbledygook. "Binobo shuf spug" means "Welcome to my world."

News Brief: Miley Cyrus Visits White House

BY Shélan O'Keefe, *Grade 10*

FROM *Know Your Onion: Writing, Journalism and Satire, Winter 2011*

74

MILEY CYRUS CREATED A SENSATION at the White House Tuesday after crashing her Hummer through the oval office window.

"I love her so much!" wept a receptionist after suffering several head injuries from the candy-pink vehicle.

It appears Miley fell asleep at the wheel after listening to her latest album.

Nerd Love

BY Sara McDufford, *Grade 3*

FROM *25 Seconds to Eat the Whole Pie, Spring 2011*

ONCE THERE WAS A GUY NAMED COURT. He was a fourth grade
nerd. He was actually the smartest kid of all. He did everything but recess because he always wanted to learn. He loved
to learn because he liked interesting math, science, and culture. He was the lamest kid at school.

The big day began when it was lunchtime and Court
was going to his locker to get his lunch. He saw bullies. The
bullies looked like vicious, mean, nasty pit bulls. Their language was like a screechy car. But the nerd defeated them
with his math book. Then a teacher came, she was walking
very speedily. She looked mean. Whenever a kid moved a
muscle she got really angry, but also once in a while she was
nice, but not too nice. When Court saw the teacher he took
a breath with a relieving sigh, "*Phew.*"

After the bullies got suspended, Court fell in love with a nerd girl named Suzy. Suzy was a nerd, but not really that smart. She had pimples on her face. Court liked her because she was nice and a little intelligent.

Suzy saw Court by his locker and didn't want to ask him if he wanted to have a playdate or not because she felt a little nervous. When she saw him the second time, she asked him if they could have lunch together. Suzy said, "I like you."

"I like you too," said Court.

They hugged, but then — *blah* — a nerd kiss. Court felt like he was in heaven when they kissed. That was Court's greatest day of his life.

Court was OK with being a nerd, but when he met Suzy, Suzy showed him skateboarding tricks. She decided to give Court some lessons. People have been saying they are a great couple.

My Friend the Frog

BY Cristian Rodriguez, *Grade 4*
FROM *25 Seconds to Eat the Whole Pie, Spring 2011*

ONE DAY I WENT TO TOYS-R-US. I went to look at my favorite toys, the Transformers. When I was walking home I saw a rainbow. I ran toward it until I got to the end of the rainbow. It didn't take long to get there because I took a bike.

Before I got to the end, I thought about something. "I think there might be some money at the end of the rainbow." I also thought there might be a black panther. I said, "I think there are just golden coins." (The coins are just usually there, but a black panther? I thought about it because of *The Jungle Book*.) I kept on biking towards the rainbow. I got to the end and found a frog.

When I found the frog, I introduced myself. It was a nice greeting. We went to jump in the pond. He taught me how to catch a fly, and then he stretched my tongue. When the frog stretched my tongue, instead of hurting, it tickled. He told me his name. It was Gary. I tested my tongue and caught a fly, but I gave it to my friend the frog because I didn't like the smell or the taste. It tasted really yucky.

Mr. Clumsy

BY Eva Lopez, *Grade 3*
FROM *Elementary Writing Camp, Summer 2011*

ONCE, THERE WAS A SUPERHERO. His name was Clumsy. He lived   79
in New York. His lair was underground. He was clumsy. His
weakness was homework. One day, there was a bank rob-
bery, and so Clumsy went over there. He tripped over a box!
Then the robber tripped over him, and the police caught the
robber.

The news reporter asked him, "Who are you?" and
he said, "I am Mr. Clumsy." Then he went to his job at the
library.

Mr. Bubbles and the Solution to the Disco Ball

BY The Students of Ms. Reynold's Class, *Grade 3*
FROM *CICS Basil, Fall 2010*

80 ONCE UPON A TIME, there was a talking latté named Mr. Bubbles. Mr. Bubbles lived in a house on 15th Avenue in Latté Village. He had chocolate legs and giant hair made out of whipped cream, and his eyes shot out of straws in his whipped cream head. Mr. Bubbles was very friendly.

Mr. Bubbles loved to talk. He spoke French. However, every time he opened his mouth, coffee came pouring out! Mr. Bubbles's arms were made out of rubber Silly Bandz. Because of this he could never clean up the coffee that he spilled. This really annoyed his cousin Mocha.

Every time Mocha tried to tell Mr. Bubbles about this, Mr. Bubbles looked at him in confusion. Mr. Bubbles had no ears and often had trouble hearing. Mocha had pumpkin arms and enormous ears, and he liked to dance.

One Friday night, Mocha invited Mr. Bubbles to go hip-hop dancing with him. However, Mr. Bubbles had had problems hip-hop dancing in the past. Whenever he opened his mouth to talk, coffee spilled all over the dance floor and people would slip and fall. Also, no one understood the French that Mr. Bubbles was speaking.

Ring, ring, ring went the phone at Mr. Bubbles's house.

Mr. Bubbles picked up the phone and said, "*Blahhhh!*"

"What did you just say?" said Mocha in reply.

"What's up?" said Mr. Bubbles, who could barely be understood from all the hot liquid coming out of his mouth.

"Do you wanna go dance with me at the Pumpkin Disco Ball?" asked Mocha.

Finally, Mr. Bubbles understood his cousin. "Yes," he answered sadly, "but I am afraid that no one will understand the French that I speak and that the coffee coming out of my mouth will make everyone trip and fall. What should I do?"

How will Mr. Bubbles talk without ruining the dance floor? Will he be able to make any friends? Where is Leslie Caron when you need her? Help our protagonist solve his problems and finally enjoy a nice evening out!

Modern Day Artist

BY Elisha Miles, *Grade 10*

A woman and her children went to a museum today.
It's hard to say how many children she had,
sometimes the woman doesn't know herself,
but when she walked into the museum she
counted three discernable bodies.
She saw marble flooring and high ceilings,
smelled sophistication and suits
and saw other women
with their better dressed
and mannered children.
She snorted at them and preceded
to walk up the multitude of stairs,
which her legs were accustomed to.

Her children had flown to the top already,

chirping her name and twittering about.
Once she reached the top,
she saw famous painters, whom she'd only heard of
in pop culture references. Most of them French.
She had no idea what the names of their most famous
    paintings were,
but remembered the images.
She remembered the images and knew they were beautiful
only because people said they were.
She stopped in front of one painting.
It had a bunch of sunflowers on it.
Ah, the sunflower guy, she mused and
her eyes noticed the golden placard with a short
biography of Vincent Van Gogh.   83
The words, which had a conversation with her eyes, were
quite conservative until they mentioned that he
cut off his left ear.

She grunted in amusement and walked on.
Hah, must be the qualifications of an artist
she smirked then thought about how nice it
would be if she were deaf.
All of those rambling nights
of noise and nagging,
sicknesses and accidents and nightmares
would be turned to silence.

The woman, Muriel, smiled at the thought.

She floated from painting to painting
while her children trailed
either behind or ahead of her
however, she always knew where they were.
It was a bit after five when she took up her children and left
with the understanding that she did not have the
      qualifications of an artist.
She was glad too. All the ones she saw were crazy.

At six she returned to the place that had no marble floors or
      high ceilings
That had no smell of sophistication or suits.
The stairs creaked as her children flitted up the steps
that moaned for Muriel as she went up to the fourth floor.
Muriel still wondered how she did it when she was
      pregnant.
She took out her keys and opened the door to home.
She uncurled her toes from her tight dress shoes and felt the
      relief
that only a cold flat floor could give to her feet.
The kids began to undress.
They took off their good clothes and Muriel
folded them back into their drawers.
Knowing that they would get a bath soon, the little ones
ran around the house in their underwear while Muriel
turned on the bathwater.
Swirls of steam met her face while
she dropped pink bath pearls and
then beckoned for them to come to the water.
Muriel peeled the remains of their garments off

and put them into the dirty clothes hamper.
She reached into the linens closet
got some towels and
then placed them on the toilet seat.

Muriel stepped quickly into the kitchen
where she felt her name being called
and then thought about what she wanted to make her
        babies.
Yeah. That'll do. She thought.
She got out a metal pot and filled it with water.
The pot banging against the sides of her sink
sounded like an underwater gong.
Muriel sat at the table her husband bought at a yard sale.
She didn't want it then because she already had one,
but right after he bought it, their kitchen table collapsed.
So they'd used this one since then.
One of the children, probably Margot, etched a house into
        the wood.
Now this is art. She thought,
why doesn't someone come into my house,
pay me money for my table
and put it in a museum?
It looks plenty good enough to me.

Once the water started to boil
she added a dash of salt to prevent the pasta from sticking
and added two boxes of tortellini to it.
Then she took out ground chuck and heated up a large
        black pan.

After the pan got nice and hot, she added the chunk of meat
to it.

It sizzled and moisture swirled out of it.

She chopped it up into little pieces until it began to brown
and seasoned it with orange and yellow salts and spices
and drained the fat out with a sieve.

By then she knew the pasta was soft and drained as well.

She put both meat and pasta into a white ceramic dish,
the one her mother gave to her on her wedding day,
and mixed pre-shredded cheese into the mix.

She put it in the oven to be baked.

By then, her children were yelping her name to get out of
the tub.

She took the towels off the toilet seat and wrapped each
child with one.

She carried the littlest one out of the tub and helped him
get into his
pajamas.

The children ran to the television in the living room until
dinner was called.

Then the children ate and were quickly put to bed for church
in the morning.

She washed the dishes and slid into her nightgown.

Muriel lay in her bed thinking of her day and the things
she accomplished.

She knelt at the bedside, said the last of her Rosary
and slipped into bed thinking herself an artist.

A Who? What? Where? When? Why? Poem

BY Sabrina Ticer-Wurr, *Grade 3*
FROM *Elementary Writing Camp, Summer 2011*

Catherine LaBriere 87
is making popcorn and playing piano at the same time
at 6:05 AM on a Sunday
on a hot-pink-and-highlighter-yellow-striped couch in her
living room
because she wanted to do that
but her parents don't let her
but they are asleep.

Michael and the Red With Blue Stripes T-Rex

BY Julian Raphael Mercado-Pacalso, *Grade 4*
FROM *Mitchell School, Fall 2010*

MICHAEL WAS WALKING to the train and he found a red with blue stripes T-Rex eating on the black train tracks. The T-Rex was in danger. The blue long train was 30 miles away. It was coming near, so he shouted to the T-Rex, "Go Away!"

The T-Rex jumped because it was a good jumper. The T-Rex ran away. Michael thought, "What is a baby dinosaur doing here?"

The next beautiful morning Michael saw the T-Rex again and asked, "Can I call you Buddy?"

The T-Rex replied, "Sure."

Buddy the T-Rex asked, "Would you like to go to my party to thank you for saving my life?"

"Sure, I love parties," Michael whispered.

"So let's go," Buddy replied.

They rode the train to the party.

"Here we are," Buddy said. "Would you like to meet my mother, Mila, and my father, Eric? " Buddy asked.

"Sure," Michael replied.

Michael and Buddy played hide and seek, tag, board games, and rested. They had chocolate cake and apple juice. Michael went home. He was happy and they continued to be friends and tell stories together.

Letter to Amy

BY Lily Beckert, *Grade 3*

FROM *Elementary Writing Camp, Summer 2011*

90

Amy, you're the stars.
Amy, you're a star.
Everytime I look at you
It's like the first time.
You are the best cat ever.
(I'm not joking.)

Love, Lily

The Lemon Method

BY Sarah Meyer, *Grade 11*

FROM *Young Writers Camp with Local Authors, Summer 2011*

THE LEMON METHOD:

Pick a verse (maybe a song lyric, some phrase you found in a magazine, or interesting sentences you've heard in the past couple days).

Write said verse acrostically: the words from the verse will be the first words for each line in your poem.

Continue each line, adding other words and whatnot to create a strange pile of enjambed lines and seemingly connected words.

Don't be afraid to write things that conflict with the original line—it's encouraged actually.

Don't be afraid to change the form of this poem once you've made it, after all this is a prompt.

And... *BOOM* there it is:

The Lemon Method.

Enjoy.

Lemon Method Poem

BY Sarah Meyer, *Grade 11*

FROM *Young Writers Camp with Local Authors, Summer 2011*

Every Family Should Have A Grandfather
Every whisper will join the
family of words ever spoken. These words would, these
words
should find refuge in our minds but instead they
have drifted away from our gravity.
A word will never linger. At least, that's what
grandfather told me.

Lemon-y Poems

BY Misa Myong, *Grade 11*

FROM *Young Writers Camp with Local Authors, Summer 2011*

At Least That's What You Said To Them   93

At the

Least put on some deodorant because

That's just

What everyone wants

You to do since they

Said you have a sweating problem and need

To keep away from

Them until the problem is resolved

Where Are The Laughing Manatees

Where my cavities derived from

Are not unknown. It all happened

The night we were

Laughing and eating

Manatees

The King of Zombie Pop

BY Lylajean Bariso, *Grade 3*

FROM *Zombies Can't Write, but Kids Can!, Spring 2011*

THERE WAS A LAZY ZOMBIE who really liked Michael Jackson. He was happy when he died (because he would be a zombie), so he looked everywhere for Michael Jackson's grave. He travelled to Los Angeles (it was hard to get into the airport!), New York (so many brains... tempting!), and even Chicago (best city ever!), but he could not find the grave. So he looked online (hard to find a computer).

The zombie found out where Michael Jackson's grave was, but he told nobody. Not even me! He dug up the grave and Michael Jackson arose.

"Augh, not again. What do you want? CD? Autograph? Interview?" Michael Jackson said.

The zombie would have fainted, but he was a zombie, so... he couldn't. He got Michael Jackson to sign his shoe, and he showed it to all of his friends. They were shocked and almost even fainted, but of course they couldn't. Yes, the zombie got to meet Michael Jackson (Yay!) and they became good friends! They always met together under a big grave.

Jorb and the Missing Giamond

BY The Students of Mrs. Jovanovich's Class, *Grade 3*

FROM *Drummond Montessori Magnet School, Fall 2010*

Hi, my name is Jorb and I live with my sister, Zyluh, and my cat, Fufu. She's very fluffy, Jorb wrote in his diary, while he was camping in a forest in Amsterdam.

Jorb's job was really intense, so he went camping to relax. He was an actor who did a lot of miming and sometimes fell off the stage and broke his nose. His sister, Zyluh, was sometimes annoying because she read his diary, but Jorb brought her camping because his mom made him. He brought Fufu because he loved her.

Jorb was in the forest because he heard that there was a large diamond buried out there somewhere. It was so big, people called it a Giamond. If Jorb found the Giamond, he could retire from acting and be happy forever.

Jorb and Zyluh decided to go look for the Giamond at night, because most people would be asleep. They brought

Fufu along on the search because Jorb had recently invented a collar that finds Giamonds.

Half a mile into the woods the collar started to vibrate, and Fufu said, "Meow! The Giamond's nearby." (The collar could also translate what Fufu said.)

Jorb looked around and saw a little bit of the Giamond sticking out of the ground, shining under the moonlight. The only problem was that in between Jorb and the Giamond was a long, rickety bridge over a lava river. And, on the other end of the bridge was a growling Hungarian dog!

Very cautiously and slowly, Jorb stepped onto the bridge. The dog growled louder, and one of the planks on the bridge snapped off and fell into the lava. Zyluh screamed.

97

How will Jorb make it across the bridge? Will he ever get the Giamond? A magyar kutyák beszélnek magyarul? It's up to you to help out Jorb and finish the story!

I Know Your Favorite Color

BY Konrad Andreasik, *Grade 3*

FROM *Abrazos de Marisposas/Butterfly Hugs*

You are as beautiful as a rose
You wear red every day, our house is all red
Your towels are all red
You're all red
The whole earth is red because your favorite
Color is red
I wear red to school even if the uniform is
white and blue
I know your favorite color is red
And I'm your favorite son Konrad Andreasik,
Kamil too
I'll make you a red rose out of paper
You'll see it after school
You take care of me and Kamil
You shine like the sun and you wear yellow

sometimes
Your eyes shine like the sun
Your hair shines like the sun
Your shoes shine like the sun
Your clothes shine like the sun because your
Other favorite color is yellow

99

I Am From

BY Mikey Hicks, *Grade 6*
FROM *25 Seconds to Eat the Whole Pie, Spring 2011*

100

From Autumn I started.
The dancing leaves on the sidewalk
the cold water on the beach
the breeze on a colorful day
the October,
my day of birth —
the time my dad remembers most.

I continued with the fun-filled days.
Full of laughter,
a day at the pool
Splish splash.
All friends and family,
a great hot dog
with some Coke, too.

Maybe some Mentos, Michelle.

I am from home,
the fresh smell at the end of the day.
a feast for a king.
The loving, caring family,
the fried chicken in my bed,
and my misfit friend, Clyde.
Also the talking bacon.

Grown

BY Raquel Raby-Newsom, *Grade 5*

I am made of my fish even though she's dead.
my friends who make me happy each day
my cat who gives me joy and hope
my brother who makes me laugh each hour.
I am made of New Mexico, Africa, Paris, Italy
dropping rain, fire crackling
The Bean
lunch and recess.
I am made from drawing my cat and thinking of her
I am a cat
I am made from my bed.
I am grown from tomatoes, herbs and much more...
pasta, pizza, salad
from violin

from walking in the rain and cuddling with my cat
I am grown from playing with
mud.

The Great Milk Floods

BY Lisa Bellisario, *Grade 6*
FROM *Mitchell School, Spring 2010*

MANY EONS AGO, in ancient Greece, a volcano erupted, killing everyone in sight, except for hundreds of cows. Ever since the Greeks' end had come, the cows started to cause big problems—especially the great milk floods. Since no one was around to milk the cows, their udders would fill up to the point where the pain was absolutely unbearable. This made the cows very angry, and so they pushed all of the milk out of their bodies as hard as they could, causing floods of milk. It was horrible. The pressure of the milk was destroying the crumbling houses and crops.

Well, one day, Emilia, the Goddess of Animals, saw this. She was not very happy. "Oh, I thought you black-and-white creatures were better and more peaceful than this!" she cried. "I have to put an end to this immediately!"

So Emilia called out the vile Chupacabra. The Chupacabra was a large and monstrous creature who was slimy and green, and had teeth like Ginsu knives. He had giant bug eyes, toothlike claws, and a big serpent tail and wings.

"My Chupacabra," the goddess called out in a loving voice, "I would like you to fly down to earth, and drink all the milk out of the cows until their udders are dried out!"

"No!" the Chupacabra shouted. "What's in it for me?" he scoffed.

Emilia took out $50 from her flowing velvet robe. Then she looked at him sternly.

"Double it!" the monster said. "Done." They shook claw and hand.

So, of course, the monster flew down to earth and did the deed. But when Jo-John, the god of food, saw this, he was steaming mad with Emilia. First, he had the Chupacabra's head cut off (but then he grew back another one and Jo-John left it alone). He stormed across Mount Olympus to confront the goddess of animals because this was very serious.

"Emilia! What in the name of Zeus were you thinking?" Jo-John screamed. The goddess was quite startled. "All of the milk has gone and now we will have nothing to pour into our golden oatmeal!"

"Well first of all, why not use our royal cows' milk? Second, did you not see what they were doing to the land? We spent a great deal of time and hard work creating it! And the cows are destroying that!" Emilia argued.

"Although the humans were a bad idea," Jo-John said under his breath.

"Oh, so is *that* why you caused that volcano to erupt and kill them? It was like Pompeii *all over again!* I mean, what is it with humans that angers you so much?" Emilia thundered back.

"They are all worthless!" shouted Jo-John.

"So then who gave us all these precious gifts? You, sir, are one greedy being!" shouted the goddess. The two of them were quarreling like an old married couple for another two hours, until the goddess of animals snapped out of it.

"Well, why are you so angry about disposing of the cows' milk?" she asked. *Come to think of it, he's always angry with me,* she thought.

"Because it is not your duty," replied the god of food.

"'Not my duty? 'Not my duty' he says!" yelled Emilia. "I am the goddess, the warden, of all animals! It is given to me that I must take care of animals and solve any problems they or we come upon with them! Henceforth; it *is* my *duty!*" Emilia was flushing pink with frustration. At that moment, there was a flash of lightning in the sky.

Meanwhile, Jo-John lay on a nearby sofa, clutching a teddy bear in fright and gaping at the goddess. When she got mad, she got *mad!*

"A-Anyuh-wh-who," he stammered, "Maybe there is a way to bring the milk back." Emilia had a hint of a smile. "By the way, I can't use our royal cow's milk because that dope of a Chupacabra drank their milk, too!" he whined. The goddess of animals snickered.

"Wait! I know just what to do!" she exclaimed with joy. "We can create humans—"

"To milk the cows!" he finished.

"And we will call them—"Emilia started to say.

"*Farmers*, because they will work on farms with the cows!" the god of food continued.

So the two gods went to work, conjuring up their powers of magic to create the farmer. In no time at all they had formed a handsome farm worker. He was a man with brown, wavy hair, blue eyes, and very clean skin. Jo-John even gave the man denim overalls and a straw hat to protect him from the sun. Emilia also created a woman for the man, so that they could marry and repopulate Greece. The two new humans worked together each day, milking the cows and having children.

"I've got to say, we have outdone ourselves," said Jo-John, admiringly looking down at the scene from his golden balcony in the clouds.

"But you said you disliked—"Emilia was interrupted by her accomplice kissing her! Jo-John kissed her a long, lingering kiss on the lips.

No wonder we were always fighting! she thought. *He's in love with me!* She placed her arms around his neck.

Soon, the earth was filled with humans, and there was never a milk flood again.

Well, my friends, this has been the tale of how farmers were created and angry cows too. This will be a story to tell generations of your family, for years and years to come. In other words...

The End

Glamimi the Squirrel's Dancing Day

BY The Students of Ms. Shane's Class, *Grade 2*
FROM *Pulaski International School of Chicago, Fall 2010*

GLAMIMI THE SQUIRREL lived in an underground warehouse, where all day long he practiced his best dance moves. He loved to dance. Glamimi always wore a red shirt and skinny jeans, and cut his hair in a green Mohawk. He also wore glasses.

Glamimi danced day after day, practicing his moves: especially break dancing and the cha-cha.

His parents told him not to dance so much, but one Monday Glamimi saw a flyer announcing a big dance tournament.

This Friday! it said. There would be all kinds of other animals, including dancing mice.

"Man, I wish I could join this tournament, but my parents would never let me," Glamimi sighed. "I'd better sneak out."

109

That Friday night, while his parents were eating a delicious dinner of Nutty Acorn Cereal, Glamimi tiptoed through the warehouse and snuck out through the window. Underneath his new red suit, Glamimi wore his special glow-in-the-dark skeleton costume for the tournament. He dug a tunnel all the way to school. 100 feet! The end of his tunnel was in the hallway of the school. He dashed through the halls to the Squirrely-Whirly Dance Studio.

When he entered the studio, Glamimi saw chicks doing the jump split, bunnies tap dancing, and cats doing head spins. Glamimi tiptoed into the room and over to the sign-up sheet.

"I'd better not use my real name," he thought. "My parents might find out." He signed the sheet, "*Rumbo Chestnut.*"

As he waited his turn, Glamimi's teeth chattered and he bit his nails. Finally, the judges called, "Rumbo Chestnut, please take the stage."

When he reached the stage, the song, "Dance Little Squirrel" began to blare from the speakers. Glamimi started to do his best moves, all at once. He was break dancing, cha-cha-ing, and doing backflips all at the same time. Just as he was about to do his grand finale move, he heard voices from the back of the studio.

"*Glamimi! Get off of that stage!*"

It was his parents!

How will Glamimi explain that squirrels just wanna have fun? Will he win the competition? Put on your writing shoes and go nuts!

Fried Orange Fiasco

BY The Students of Ms. Lohitsa's Class, *Grade 6*
FROM *Randolph Magnet School*

SANDY THE SLOTH was in the middle of another busy day at her restaurant, Fast Orange Frenzy. Although Sandy was a sloth, she was the fastest sloth in the world and was very efficient at peeling the oranges with her long black fingernails and then frying them at lightning speed. Sandy had her curly hair tied back and wore safety goggles to prevent getting orange juice in her eyes. The goggles were blue and matched her tank top, but her pants had one orange leg and one purple leg.

The restaurant was crowded with all the other animals who lived in Calijungle, a city deep in the rainforest. The fried oranges were flying. Then in came Fred. Fred was a very wealthy white orangutan who had made all his money dancing in the circus. He wore a black tuxedo and fancy shoes, and he carried a cane. He had pulled up in a limousine driven by his chauffeur, a zebra, and accompanied by

111

an entourage of tamarins. Fred frequently ate at Fast Orange Frenzy, and he ordered baskets of fried oranges by the thousands. He burst through the doors and into the restaurant, and his tamarin friends played Fred's theme song (he had his own theme song) on trumpets. The other animals' jaws dropped. Fred was not only wealthy, but famous. All the young animals in Calijungle ran up to him when he was out and about and asked for his autograph.

Sandy was so happy and nervous that she dropped the orange she was peeling on the floor. She could smell Fred's strawberry-banana cologne all the way from the kitchen.

"Me want oranges!" Fred shouted. "Oranges for everyone, on me!"

Sandy ran into the dining room, and nervously pulled out a chair for Fred.

"Please sit down, sir," she stammered.

"One thousand oranges!" Fred demanded.

"Yes, sir, right away, sir," Sandy said shyly. Fred waved his hand, which was covered in diamond rings, to shoo Sandy away. Fred didn't really like sitting in a restaurant crowded with all the other animals from Calijungle; he was certain that he was better than them, and preferred only the company of his tamarin friends.

Sandy ran back to the kitchen in a panic. She was running low on oranges that day and only had 30 of them in the refrigerator. She called to her two head chefs, Sammy and Rigby, "Guys! I need you to go out into the rainforest and get 970 oranges for me, on the fly!"

The problem was that Sammy and Rigby were also sloths, but unlike Sandy, were not the fastest sloths in the world. When they headed out with their giant baskets, Sandy knew it might be a long wait before they returned with the oranges Fred had demanded.

Sandy put on her bravest sloth face and combed out her curly hair with her long claws. She cleared her throat and headed back out into the dining room.

The dining room was in a state of chaos. The customers were all hungry, and pounding on the tables chanting, "Oranges! Oranges!" Fred was sitting with his arms crossed, glaring around the room.

Sandy said to Fred, "My chefs are out getting more oranges for you, but the thing is, we weren't expecting such a large order today, so it might be—well—a bit of a wait."

"Well then, I shall wait," Fred growled. "But I am not happy about this."

"In the meantime, can I offer you an appetizer of frozen mashed pineapple?"

"Lovely," said Fred. "But really, I came here to make a proposition."

"What's that, sir?" Sandy asked.

"Don't you hate having to deal with this riff-raff?" Fred asked, gesturing at the yelling customers.

"These are my friends," Sandy said. "They are usually much nicer."

"It's crowded, tacky, hectic, noisy, and messy, and you have to serve so many animals. Why don't you come be my personal chef at my mansion? I have a big pool, tamarin friends to bring us an unlimited supply of oranges, 17 cars, and lots of blue dresses and shoes for you."

"I could never do that," Sandy cried. "What would my waiters and my chefs do for jobs? And where would my customers get their fried oranges if I closed my doors?"

"I'm sorry, I can't let you bring your friends," Fred grumbled. "You could just fire them."

"I can't take you up on the offer then, I'm sorry," Sandy replied.

"You know, I'm a powerful orangutan. If I put out the word that I had to wait for 17 hours for my fried oranges and that I saw a cockroach on the floor, this place would be deader than the dinosaurs," Fred said craftily.

"You can't do that!" Sandy cried. "I don't care how much money you have, my friends love Fried Orange Frenzy."

But Sandy was scared. She didn't want to lose the restaurant, so she agreed to go with Fred to the mansion for a little while, until she could figure out a plan to escape. She put a "Closed Until Further Notice" sign on the door of the restaurant.

Sandy wasn't happy at the mansion, even though she had a blue car to drive and blue dresses to wear and a blue pool to swim in. She missed the fast pace of the restaurant, and missed Sammy and Rigby, whom she didn't get to say goodbye to because they were still searching for the 970 oranges when she left. Sandy even missed the noisy and crowded dining room.

One morning she was feeling especially lonely, when she heard the sound of chanting. "Oranges, oranges, oranges."

Sandy ran to the window, and she saw everyone who had ever eaten at Fast Orange Frenzy, which was almost everyone in Calijungle, coming up the hill to the mansion. They threw open the doors and played a theme song they had written for Sandy, on trumpets.

When Fred saw how much Sandy had been missed, he decided to stop being selfish and let her go. Fred came to love the "riff-raff," and from then on always ate his fried oranges at Fast Orange Frenzy—and always tipped the waitresses.

115

Flammable Objects Before a Forest Fire

BY Darius Vinesar, *Grade 6*
FROM *Solomon School, Fall 2010*

ONE BEAUTIFUL NIGHT in Foodland, two friends were roaming about in Mushroom Forest in the wilds of Hawaii. The two friends were a tiny pea and a large potato. The potato was called Giovanni de Patche la Magnifico. The pea was called Bob. They both worked in a box factory where they made boxes.

Their boss, a fat cabbage, said they could go on vacation instead of having a raise. The two friends packed immediately and left the next morning. They arrived at the Hotel of Food Exquisite at noon, and planned a beautiful group hike in Mushroom Forest led by a carrot guide. They checked their equipment and set off into the forest. After they walked a little, the guide told everybody not to stray from the path or else. But a few minutes later something caught Bob's eye. Bob ran into the forest and Giovanni chased him while telling him to stop. But their guide and their group simply didn't hear them and they walked farther and farther away.

Finally Giovanni caught up with Bob. Bob turned around and said, "I thought I saw somethin'." Giovanni ignored him and looked for the path. They searched hours and hours but did not find it. It started getting dark so Giovanni said, "Let's just rest for the night. I'm tired." And Bob said, "I agree with you."

They found a clearing and set up a fire. The night was chilly and there was a cold breeze that ruffled the leaves. While they were warming themselves up by the small fire, Giovanni took out a can of bug spray and sprayed himself.

"Can I have some of that too?" asked Bob.

Giovanni gave the can of spray to Bob. Bob sprayed himself and gave it back. Then Bob said, "Hey, I dare you to throw that can into the fire."

Giovanni looked at the can and said, "I don't know man. It says it's flammable. It might be dangerous."

Bob took the spray can and threw it into the fire. The fire roared and set a leaf on fire.

"Oh, man! We better stop that fire!" said Giovanni.

"Nah, just leave it. The wind will blow it out!" said Bob. But soon the whole branch caught on fire. Giovanni looked nervous and his head was slick with sweat.

"Oh, man! It's getting bigger!" said Giovanni.

"Just leave it. I told you, the wind will blow it out," said Bob.

But the whole tree caught on fire. The tree was visible in the boiling, raging inferno that soon caught other trees on fire. By then it was too late to stop it. Soon the whole Mushroom Forest was blazing in the night. The next morning two humans walked by the burnt remains of the forest and found a nice meal of baked potatoes and peas.

Fish Day

BY Juan Jimenez, *Grade 3*

FROM *25 Seconds to Eat the Whole Pie, Spring 2011*

YESTERDAY, I invented a new holiday called Fish Day. On Fish   119
Day we celebrate the fish that cats eat. We also celebrate the
cats because they are smart. All day cats use their claws to
grab fish swimming in a small tank. Each cat gets its own
tank and it has to be pretty small or the cats wouldn't go by
it because they hate water. Their paws shake the water so
it looks like the fish are alive. On Fish Day, people sleep on
rugs and cats sleep on beds.

Every day, my cat says she would like to drive the car.
On Fish Day I let her. She will go and get her friends and go
to the cat mall so they can buy things. I don't know what but
maybe shirts or some boots. And after that she will home
and take a nap.

PS: On the bed.

Everyone Is Happy

BY Lauren Alaniz, *Grade 2*

FROM *I Need Everyone to See My Sparkles, Winter 2011*

CAROLINE LIKES TO PAINT on her beautiful back porch where the sun shines. She has long black hair, with bits of red in it, and a black-and-pink bow. Her favorite things to paint are mermaids because she thinks they're pretty and she loves them. She loves to sing while she's painting.

Every Tuesday at one o'clock in the morning, her friends come over and they have a band. They only play slow jazz. Her husband comes to watch and says, "I would love to hear you sing." And she is very nice, and sings.

They have a party every day at Caroline's blue mansion, and then they all eat cheesecake. Her friends—the queen of England, a kid in a mustache, President Obama, and a pencil named Connor—are all there. They have pepperoni pizza and a couple hot dogs. After everyone eats they feel really good and full. Some of them even feel sick. So they all sit on the huge plain white couch and watch a little bit of TV. It is a movie called *The Dinosaur.* They like this movie because Coltrane, their favorite actor, is in it. And then they all go home and read their kids a story and go to bed. Since the mothers do the most work, they are the ones who get to read the stories, so they pick Dora.

And the next day, everyone goes out in Caroline's boat and has a wedding for Caroline's friend. Her friend is wearing a beautiful white dress and a veil that looks like a crown. The bride and groom kiss and a great big wave splashed everyone on the boat. Then the fireworks go off and everyone is happy.

Doris the Ice Cream Hero

BY The Students of Ms. Brady's Class, *Grade 3*

FROM *CICS Washington Park, Winter 2011*

ONCE UPON A TIME there was a horse named Doris who was extremely good at math. She had brown and black stripes, and she could fly. Doris lived on the planet Ice Creamia, which was covered in ice cream. Doris's job was to protect the ice cream on Ice Creamia from ice cream stealing space pirates from Mars.

One day, Doris woke up in her house made of mint ice cream and ate a breakfast of chocolate chip ice cream. Then, she walked five miles through a field of ice cream boulders and through a swamp of melted ice cream to get to work. Doris worked from a secret hideout where she kept an eye on space from a giant telescope.

At work, Doris saw her friend, Milky the cow. He had the power to turn invisible.

"Hello, Milky! Are you ready to work today?" Doris said.

"Yes, Doris. I'm ready to work. But we have a problem," Milky said.

"Oh, no! What's the problem?" asked Doris.

Milky said, "I saw something way off in the distance. I'm afraid it might be some of those ice-cream-stealing pirates."

As Doris and Milky watched, the ship got closer. It was a flying boat with vegetable-shooting cannons, because everyone on Ice Creamia was allergic to vegetables. On the sail of the boat it said "Give Us Ice Cream."

The ice-cream-stealing pirates were green monkeys, who desperately wanted to steal the ice cream.

"We need to come up with a plan! Quick!" Doris said.

The flying ship was getting closer and closer! Doris decided to fly out toward the ship to see what the monkeys were planning.

She saw the cannon full of vegetables, packed with carrots, corn, and lettuce, ready to fire at Ice Creamia. Doris used her special math skills to determine when the ship would get to her planet and start to fire. She also figured out where the vegetables would land and how fast they would be coming.

"I figured out when the ice-cream-stealing pirates will get here and where the vegetables will land," Doris said to Milky.

But what Doris and Milky had not planned on was the sudden ice cream blizzard! Suddenly and without warning, gallons of chocolate ice cream began falling out of the sky.

123

Much to their dismay, Doris and Milky could no longer see where the space pirates were—or where they were headed.

"*Aaaaarrrrrrggghhhh!!!!*" screamed Milky and Doris at the same time.

Can Doris and Milky stop the aliens? What will happen to the vegetable cannon? Could somebody pass the chocolate syrup and sprinkles? Help our characters save Ice Creamia as you write your own sweet ending!

124

Edward Gorey's Dead Brain Children and the Breakdown of Modern Language (Again)

BY Phoebe Murtagh, *Grade 9*
FROM *Everything There Is, Fall 2010*

Thirteen little Edwardian girls,
and the same amount of small, curious boys;
lined up on cold gravestones,
like Gorey's illustrated puppet toys.

And the same amount of small, curious boys,
dead to the world,
like Gorey's illustrated puppet toys.
Lost like our words.

Dead to the world,
like Gorey's illustrated puppet toys
Lost like our words;
they weren't marionettes.

Morbidly, amusingly misused;
thirteen little Edwardian girls.
They weren't marionettes,
lined up on cold stone graves.

Do Not Let Anyone Hit You With a Cabbage

BY Jalina Garay, *Grade 4*
FROM *BLAM! You're There, Spring 2011*

Dear Rahm Emanuel,

I am ten years old. I have four people in my family. I have a dog and his name is Bear. Bear's color is black and white. I have blond and brown hair, brown eyes. Do not let anyone hit you with a cabbage just like what they did to William Howard Taft.

For the students who are in school, do not let them get extra work or homework. If I did not have homework, I would be so happy and I would read a book, draw, play with my dog, go to the mall, and I would have a lot of fun. I would read *The Babysitter's Club* and *Diary of a Wimpy Kid*.

Do you like making laws? You should make a law that you would give $15,000 million to me. I would save all of my money.

Sincerely,
Jalina

Diamante Poem

BY Yesenia E. Vélez, *Grade 4*

FROM *Elementary Writing Camp, Summer 2011*

My sister   129
cool, fun
babysitting, shopping, singing
talented, motherly, Marines, handsome
dancing, nursing, fighting
funny, dumb
My brothers

Dear Bah

BY Nora Thomas, *Grade 3*

FROM *Elementary Writing Camp, Summer 2011*

130 YOU WERE THE BEST. I wish you lived forever. I could see you as a cat queen. I wish you could read, write, and eat anything. I would teach you how to get along with dogs. You would usually listen to us. But why wouldn't you listen all the time?

The Day Michael Jackson Turned My Life Around

BY Ella Watson, *Grade 6*
FROM *I Forgot to Make You Breakfast, Fall 2010*

I GOT UP AND INSTANTLY KNEW it was going to be a bad day be- cause every day was a bad day for me. My back was hurting because I fell out of my wooden, nail-y bed and couldn't find my blue T-shirt. My mom, like always, screamed, "Get down the stairs right now!" and down I went. I walked to school like usual and stepped in dog poo.

I was starving because my mom kicked me out the door before I could eat. At school, I ate the worst food ever, which was rotten bananas and spaghetti cereal with worm sauce.

Into class I went. The 70-year-old teacher, who dressed like she was 17 and smelled like armpits, said, "Today, class, we are going to have a helper!"

I said in my head, "Oh, no!"

Out from nowhere, Michael Jackson did a moonwalk into our classroom. I was so happy. He was singing the song

"Smooth Criminal" all day and I never got tired of it. He gave me his sparkling shoes (because my shoes had dog poo on them), and with the sparkling shoes he taught me how to do the moonwalk. I was so excited that I screamed at the top of my lungs. MJ was so happy that I could moonwalk that he grabbed me and spun me in the air.

Then all the kids got mad because I had sparkly shoes and they did not have any, so they turned into fairies! They put pixie dust on Michael Jackson to make him fly and he flew to the moon and now he lives there. Before MJ left, the fairies took all his fanciest clothes and threw them out the window. He was heartbroken.

If you think that MJ died from what you heard on the news, it is not true, this is what really happened to him. I still have the sparkly shoes, and now I do the moonwalk to school everyday. But every day, I clean parts of his clothes that the fairies threw out the window and I believe that he will come back from the moon.

The Day I Saw Aliens

BY Catherine Galvan, *Grade 3*

FROM *I Need Everyone to See My Sparkles, Fall 2010*

ONE NORMAL DAY I was playing a game as usual when all of a sudden I saw a green light outside of my window. I was scared at first, and then I was not for some reason.

I went outside and the light was far away. It was green and I got closer to it. It was an alien! They were big like giants and they felt like wallpaper. Their mouths were circles. They had no noses and their eyes were yellow. But I was not scared. (If other people were with me they would come out running.)

I was walking through the forest when my mind went blank because of the aliens. Then I beat up an alien. An army of them started to attack but then I beat them all up. I was pretty lucky to be in karate class. No wonder my mom wanted me to be in it. I think she was involved with these aliens. I decided I'd ask her after I finished beating up all these aliens—wait, I was done.

I went inside and my mom was making pumpkin pie. I asked her, "Are you involved with all of the alien stuff?"

My mom answered, "Maybe I am. Maybe I am not."

Then I went to my room to figure out who was involved with this instead of my mom. I kept asking my mom the same question over and over, and the same answer came out of her mouth.

Finally she said, "I am involved with all the alien stuff."

She also said, "Well, honey pie, the aliens were my friends and I wanted you to meet them. They just came to say hi to you and me."

I felt sad because I beat up my mom's alien friends. Then she invited them over for the evening and I said "sorry" and we became friends.

Clothes in a Volcano

BY Derek Finney, *Grade 7*
FROM *Solomon School, Fall 2010*

THE STORY BEGINS in a land where ice cream ate people. In that 135 land was a village in the middle of the Atlantic Ocean. In the village there was a sweet kid named Bustin Jieber. He wasn't the sharpest tool in the shed, so it was a good thing they didn't own a shed. One day, in a whiney voice Bustin said, "I want ice cream!" So his mom gave him money to go and buy some.

Later that day, he threw the unfinished ice cream on the floor in his room. His mom told him to clean it up, but he said he'd clean it up tomorrow. And the next day he did the same thing. Ice cream after ice cream piled over the piles of dirty laundry that Bustin had also thrown onto the floor. The same went on the next day and the next day for a year, until Bustin's room became a mountain of melted, sticky, vanilla ice cream!

Finally, one night when it was very dark out, the ice cream mutated into a mushy monster dressed in dirty laundry and ate Bustin Jieber. When his mom came upstairs to see if Bustin had cleaned up the mountain of ice cream yet, there was just a monstrous mush mass that burped loudly at her and moved toward her as if to eat her next. Before she could call for help, the crazed ice cream blob blobbed down the stairs, out the front door, and all the way to Hawaii, stopping only to pose to a passing ship as a melting glacier in the middle of the ocean.

Once in Hawaii, the menacing mountain of calories sent a line of hula dancers screaming for their lives and not screaming for ice cream. Then before anyone could stop it, the clothed blob of dumped ice cream jumped into an active volcano. Sweet Bustin Jieber was no more.

Chickenless Eurasia

BY Cherokee Sperry, *Grade 7*

FROM *It Came Beneath 826CHI, Summer 2011*

NARRATOR: Hide your chicken, America. You might be the next nation to know the terror of the terrorizing monster, Sir Spoiled Chicken. He was once a man. He moved to Bhutan after being deported from Bali for eating the Duke of Bali's chicken. Now, after eating a spoiled piece of chicken, he is a 500 foot tall leg of spoiled chicken who prefers Church's biscuits!

SIR SPOILED: BWA-HA-HA! I will rid the gluttonous world of chicken. HA! If they only knew where I'll strike next!

NARRATOR: This is never before seen footage of Sir Spoiled Chicken eliminating all of Bhutan's chicken. Bhutan has only one Kentucky Fried Chicken, and here he is! Eating all the chicken! It is his plan to destroy the world by chicken extinction!

FRENCH WOMAN [French accent]: No more? All the French chickens are gone? Ahhh! My restaurant will close!

Sir Spoiled Chicken crushes the Eiffel Tower.

GERMAN REPORTER: [German accent] Germany's chicken supply has been devoured!

RUSSIAN REPORTER: [Russian accent] Russia's chicken supply has been devoured!

ENGLISH REPORTER: [English accent] England's chicken supply has been devoured!

The European Union is having a meeting to discuss how to defeat Sir Spoiled Chicken.

TIN TIN: We must recruit five Americans to come to Europe and eat him.

EUROPEAN UNION: We'll have a vote.

NARRATOR: The world's fate rests in the EU's decision. What will they choose?

Cheer for Nothing

BY Audrey Pettigrew, *Grade 4*

FROM *Zombies Can't Write, But Kids Can!, Spring 2010*

CARTWHEELS, BACKFLIPS, ROUND OFFS, PYRAMIDS. She just could not do them. Stiff-necked, no-brained it was impossible for Amber to do normal stuff. After all, she was a zombie.

Oh, how hard they were on her! One day during practice, she tried to do the splits. Her leg broke off. A cartwheel and an arm came off. A back flip. Her head came off. A pyramid. A round off. Another arm, another leg, and then . . . dust, nothing more.

ChatChat the Chatty Orange

BY The Students of Miss Moore's Class, *Grade 3*
FROM *Randolph Magnet School, Winter 2011*

ONCE UPON A TIME in the very far off and exciting Land of Cheese, there lived an orange. He wasn't just any normal orange: he had the wings of a hummingbird and a monkey tail, and he possessed the amazing ability to talk all the time. His name was ChatChat and he talked so much that everyone in the Land of Cheese thought he was just a little bit obnoxious.

Everyday, ChatChat would leave the Mars Cheese Castle and go out in search of food. He would go fly around the cheese tree orchards, where grilled cheese grew like fruit on the branches. On his way there he would talk to anybody and everybody he saw.

All ChatChat ever talked about was cheese. It was insanely boring because they lived in Cheese Land—everyone knew there was cheese there!

One day, as ChatChat was on his way to the cheese tree orchard, he came across a camel named Jack.

"What's cheesin', Jack!" hollered ChatChat.

"What up? You look like a very delicious orange," Jack replied.

"I cheese your pardon!" said ChatChat.

"You look so delicious that I think I am going try to eat you." And with that, Jack the camel made a big chomping noise, "CHOMPP!" right at ChatChat.

"OH NO!" screamed ChatChat, and with that he started flying away. He flew into one of the grilled cheese trees but didn't count on one thing: the tree was made of cheese. Jack followed on the ground and caught up with him!

"I've caught up with you now!" laughed Jack. "You think you are so smart, but guess what!"

And with that, Jack started eating the tree. He chewed and chewed right through it and it fell down. So did ChatChat! In the fall ChatChat hurt his wing and couldn't fly away.

141

Knock knock. Who's there? Orange. Orange who? Orange you hoping that ChatChat escapes? We are, too! Put your pencil to work and help keep our hero from becoming fruit salad!

The Cat That Slept on a Cake

BY Ian Forbes, *Grade 3*
FROM *Elementary Writing Camp, Summer 2011*

142   THE DAY BEFORE MY BIRTHDAY, my cat slept on my cake. I flipped over the cake and it landed on my cat! The cat woke up and freaked out. He jumped off the table and ran into a wall. He passed out and then he woke up in my trashcan. And then I dumped him on the floor in the morning.

He thought it was his worst nightmare. He learned not to sleep on a cake.

The Beetle Project

BY Anson Xu, *Grade 8*

FROM *Healy School, Spring 2011*

THE BEETLE PROJECT TOOK PLACE back in second grade at Healy, when I was still a scaredy-cat. Now that I think about it, I find it silly and amusing for me to be scared of something that's the size of my fingernail. But of course, if it weren't for the brave side of me that stepped in, I would still be a wuss. Therefore, I'm really thankful towards this project, which made me uncover that spark of courage.

"Okay, class, we'll be starting the Beetle Project today," Ms. Yuen, my second grade teacher, announced to the class. I sneaked a glance towards the brown boxes laid on the floor next to the counter. Ms. Yuen continued, "Each of you will receive a beetle egg, a plastic container to keep your beetles, and a few pinches of this," she held up a Ziploc bag with oatmeal-like materials inside.

I froze. *Beetle? We are going to raise beetles?*

I've never liked those ugly little things and I'm afraid to even get close to them (thanks to a certain movie called *Indiana Jones: Temple of Doom*). My thoughts all crashed into one another and I began to panic. *Having to raise them + looking at beetles crawl all over with those prickly legs + having them stare at me with pitch-black eyes and getting distracted by their mouthparts + tainting my eyes with the sight of their hard, crunchy insect bodies + recalling people digesting them in* Indiana Jones = *makes-you-want-to-throw-up* DISGUSTING. Now, how in the world am I suppose to raise a beetle without me dying first—murdered by my own thoughts?

I took a deep breath and braced myself as Ms. Yuen stopped in front of me. She handed me a small cylindrical container with a small egg inside and walked on. I stared at it for a moment, feelings of terror and uncertainty slowly building up inside me. Then, cautiously, I turned to my classmate next to me and whispered, "Hey, aren't you creeped out by this?"

She faced me and replied, "No, I think this is kind of fun, I can't wait to see how the beetle's gonna grow." She smiled, eyes glowing with excitement.

After hearing this, I thought to myself. *Maybe... if I just try to approach this with an open mind... maybe, if I just try to free myself from biased thoughts and made up fears, I would be able to rid myself of this cowardly attitude...*

So, with my new resolve, I faced the project with a positive attitude. Or at least I tried. Every day, for about a month, we would observe our transforming beetles in their bottles and record down what we saw. I watched my beetle as it grew and morphed day by day from an egg to an adult.

For the first several days of the process, I dealt with my beetle carefully, still hesitant. So many different emotions were bottled up inside me as I watched it hatch from its egg into a larva; anxiety, curiosity, worry, excitement. *(As for the fright, I can't say that I wasn't afraid of the beetle at all.)* Still, with my resolve in mind, I swallowed up my fears and tried to ignore them as much as I could. *I've decided to change myself, so I've got to stick with it; or else I'll be a coward for the rest of my life. And I don't want that.*

It took a while, but after spending time with my beetle day by day, I got used to it. Through my persistence and effort of keeping the thought, *I love beetles*, in my head at all times, I succeeded in tricking myself into loving the beetle.

By the time it had reached its third growth stage and become a pupa, I no longer feared the beetle. Instead, I forged an imaginary friendship between us. I would talk to the beetle every day, sharing my laughter and troubles with it. Since it couldn't talk, I would also invent responses from the beetle to keep our conversation going.

After all our beetles reached the last stage of the growth cycle, followed by a quiz, we had to say goodbye to them. Before I released it onto the spring grass, I gazed at my beetle and murmured, "I'm glad that I had met you, thank you for being my friend." With this, I opened the cap on the container and freed my beetle. As I watched it fly away, I wished it a happy and long life.

My beetle friend is probably dead by now, but it still lives tucked away in small corner of my most precious memories. Through this experience, I've finally figured out that it is possible to overcome fears—it just takes some self-consent and time. When the time comes, if it ever does, for me to have to deal with another weakness of mine, I will definitely remember my beetle friend and the lesson it taught me.

Beach

BY Ethan Dooley, *Grade 3*

FROM *Elementary Writing Camp, Summer 2011*

Wave crashing to the shore
People surfing all around
I felt so lonely

Be Careful if You Raise the Tax

BY Anjel Melendez, *Grade 4*

FROM *25 Seconds to Eat the Whole Pie, Spring 2011*

148

Dear Rahm Emanuel,

My name is Anjel. Be careful if you raise the tax—then people will be mad at you like the Egyptians. So keep the tax about $20 a month. That way people will not be angry at you.

If I were mayor I would give cupcakes to the USA and keep the tax as low as you can. And by the way, I am ten years old. Also, good luck being mayor.

Sincerely,
Anjel

PS: Write back.

Apocalypse Not Now

BY Henry Barrett, *Grade 8*

FROM *Know Your Onion: Writing, Journalism, and Satire, Winter 2011*

ELDER GODS MOVE END OF WORLD BACK TWO WEEKS

IN A COUNCIL OF THE GREAT OLD ONES, Elder Gods of All, held last Tuesday, it was decided that the most unholy, inevitable demise of all beings would occur two weeks after the original date, December 21, 2012. "We've just got a lot of stuff on our plates right now," Dagon explained when asked why the deadline was shifted. "We're still debating how exactly it'll happen. Mosdefus wants everyone to spontaneously get stabbed by rogue chickens. That's so him. Sometimes I wonder who died and made him god of rogue chickens!"

When asked about this, Mosdefus only rolled his eyes.

"Also, the Oscars are coming up. That is always a big time for us," Dagon added before retreating to his home, the sunken city of R'lyeh in the deep recesses of the sea.

"But believe me—it's still coming. The human race is still doomed."

A press conference is expected to be held next Monday, detailing the exact reasoning for the delay and re-explaining the five-part plan for Ragnarok.

"A LOT OF TIMES when this type of thing happens the apocalypse sort of goes to the back of everyone's minds," said Argyle Brown, chairman of the Federal Apocalyptic Response Committee. "All of a sudden, it's like, nobody cares anymore. We just want people to know that the end of the world is still a major threat."

Many people who carry signs warning of the impending doom switched to "THE END IS *ALMOST* UPON US," signs. It was noted, by the way, that the new doomsday would be January 4, 2013, changing the actual year of the end of the world.

"The Mayans didn't really factor in what we thought. We have feelings, too, you know," explained someone close to the Elder Gods.

"Doom is coming," warned Dagon. "Mark my words, mortals!"

THE 5 STEPS: THE SIGN THAT DOOM HAS ARRIVED

1 Everyone will sing "Thriller" and do the dance and look like zombies.

2 Every McDonald's will burst into flames.

3 Everyone will be subjected to a multiple-choice test.

4   Something vague and unfortunate will occur.

5   Earth will turn into a bunny, and that bunny will
    proceed to devour itself.

The Amazing Tail

BY Bryan Montalban, *Grade 5*

FROM *25 Seconds to Eat the Whole Pie, Spring 2011*

ON MY 11TH BIRTHDAY, I noticed a tail behind me. It was red and blue. I was surprised because it could help me go super fast and fly. It was like a fan, it blew air in front of people's faces because they were hot and sweaty. My tail was also super stretchy. My stretchy tail was for when someone falls off of a building—I could catch them! My tail could also reflect things like gunshots.

On July 12, 2011, I was outside the White House looking at the president through the window, waiting until he invited me in. He was working on making a water park that was as big as two mansions, and he fell because he was rocking and the chair leg broke. He almost fell back to the floor, but I saved him from falling with my tail. He told his guards to let me in and he invited me for dinner.

He asked me how I got my tail and I said, "IDK."

The president said, "What does that mean?" and I said, "It means 'I don't know.'" Then I told him to study his short words.

We ate some spaghetti with meatballs. It was delicious. While we were eating, we were talking about how to make people grow more hair. Then, after we finished, I left because he was asleep in the chair.

I first discovered my tail because I started imagining it could do those things. So then I tried to see if it was true. Now I'm imagining that my tail has lasers; I tried it and it does. I use it for melting metal and anything else. Now I can be a superhero! I just need a cape or a mask.

Since I like my tail, I will try to make some for people and open a store. I will call it "Tails for Humans."

POSTFACE

An essential part of the stories in the *Compendium* is the inspired and intrepid work of our volunteers who support the words of 826CHI students at every turn. This support ranges from weekly tutoring in all homework subjects to thoughtful feedback on personal statements. It also comes from the likes of donning a neckerchief and teaching action-packed lessons on nautical terminology, for one never knows when the high seas will beckon and words like "gybe" and "mizzenmast" will come in handy. To all the 826CHI volunteers, we are sincerely grateful. You are truly the heart and soul behind all we do.

For their incredible help in this year's *Compendium* review, we thank Ashley Brand, Micki Burton, Sean Conner, Jeni Crone, Irene Gallego, Lauren Gill, Theo Hahn, Brenna

Ivey, Jean Khut, Aparna Puppala, Danny Resner, Kara Thorstenson, Julia Ventola. Our great thanks also to Laura Mittelstaedt and Billie Pritzker for spending the summer in tireless prep for this process. Fitzgerald misses you daily.

We have been nothing short of amazed by the talent and enthusiasm displayed by this year's interns at 826CHI. Cassie Cleary, Michelle Czarnecki, Angelica Davila, Lauren Gill, Jessica Gordon, Mo Hickey, Amanda Mather, Courtney Muller, Chris Rife, Francisco Tirado, Rufus Urion, Shannon Wilson, and Jim Withington, it's a privilege to work with you. Thanks for every early morning, for your much appreciated contributions, and for the countless pages of students writing you have typed in draft after draft after draft.

For her creativity and innovative vision, we are grateful to our designer Mollie Edgar. Our great thanks also to Alison True for her thorough and thoroughly-appreciated proofreading.

This book was made possible through the generosity of an anonymous donor. Your support, and your belief in the words of so many young writers, remains invaluable. Thank you for helping so many students continue to share their stories with 826CHI, with each other, and with the world at-large.

Our thanks to the many teachers and families who have connected thousands of young writers with 826CHI and helped us spread the word and excitement. We couldn't ask for better partners.

Most especially, our colossal thanks to the many young writers who have shared their writing with all of us at 826CHI. We are humbled every day by the hilarity and thoughtfulness you carry in your hearts, heads, and pencils. Your words continue to inspire. Keep writing.

—The 826CHI staff (presented here, like the pieces in the book, in reverse alphabetical order by title):

Sandy Moy, Programs Assistant
Kendra Curry, Program & Volunteer Coordinator
Patrick Shaffner, Director of Outreach & Communications
Zach Duffy, Director of Development
Kait Steele, Director of Education
Molly Walsh, Boring Store Head Agent

VOLUNTEERS, TUTORS, INTERNS, & WORKSHOP INSTRUCTORS

The suspiciously talented and remarkably generous individuals behind each and every aspect of 826CHI

Annie Aaker
Anthony McGuff
Abboreno
Lauren Abbott
Patrick Abbott
Jani Actman
Alya Adamany
Alexa Adams
Carrie Adams
Jill Adamson
Janet Adamy
Tadd Adcox
Eliza Adelson
Aaron Adler
Karla Aguilar
Anisha Ahluwalia
Jodi Akst
Anaheed Alani
Katherine Albing
Arias Aldo
Elizabeth Alexander
Ariel Alexovich
Hassan Ali
Kelsey Allen
Leah Allen
Leslie Allotta
Elmer Almachar
Joel Alonzo
Andy Alper
Carolyn Alterio
Jenna Altobelli

David Amaral
Omowale Amoin
Amy Amoroso
Jenny An
Britte Anchor
Chelise Anderson
Ellie Anderson
Jenele Anderson
Lisa Anderson
Taylor Anderson
Matt Anglen
Rachel Angres
Gina Anselmo
Aaron Apple
Beverly Applebaum
Noah Applebaum
Caroline Arata
Nile Arena
Nathan Argall
Patrick Armitage
Nathan Armstrong
Torrey Armstrong
Rachel Arndt
Nathan Arnold
Andie Arthur
Walter Askew
Kimberly Austin
Elizabeth Bagby
Yasmine Baharloo
George Baird
Assel Baitassova

Carroll Baker
Greg Baldino
Catie Ballard
Lindsay Baloun
Rhiannion Barbour
Aimee Barker
Claire Barner
Jennifer Barnes
Elisabeth Barnick
Giselle Barone
Erik Barragan
Lori Barrett
Sam Barrett
Terence Barthel
Eric Bartholomew
Don Bartlett
Melissa Barton
Shawnee Barton
Josh Bartz
Aaron Bass
Felicia Bassett
Khloe Battle
Jonathan Baude
Halle Bauer
Sara Bauer
Danielle Bauman
Nate Baumgart
Dan Baxter
Casey Bayer
Rowan Beaird
David Beazley

Anjali Becker
Billy Becker
James Behrens
Rebecca Behrens
Nancy Behrman
Mark Beidelman
Kate Bek
Ian Belknap
Emily Bell
Quinnetta Bellows
Kimberly Bellware
David Ben-Arie
Amina Benloucif
Frank Bentley
Adam Berg
Esther Bergdahl
Jillian Berger
Sherri Berger
Nicole Berland
Amy Bernstein
David Berthy
Lauren Besser
Becky Bettinger
Shelu Bhandari
Anoop Bhat
Omkar Bhatt
Ronjon Bhattacharya
Paul Biasco
Arielle Bielak
Adam Bienvenu
Shanita Bigelow
Demian Birkins
Jennifer Bisbing
Andrew Bishop
Eric Bjorlin
Megan Black
Shomari Black
Harry Blacklock
Julie Blacklock
Emily Blaha

Edward Blair
Daniel Blake
David Blatt
Amy Blevins
Lorne Bobren
Danielle Bochneak
Nicole Bock
Christy Bockheim
Allison Bogner
Kyren Bogolub
Kate Boisseau
Margaret Bolin
Anna Bolm
Ana Bolotin
Kat Bolton
Celina Bondie
Loren Bondurant
Mark Bonus
Greg Boose
Dove Boyko
Becky Boyle
Ryan Boyle
Elizabeth Boyne
Jeffery Bozeman
Andrea Bozinovich
Jennifer Bozyk
Becca Bradley
Daniel Brady
Aaron Brager
Sangini Brahmbhatt
Ashley Brand
Jennifer Brandel
Katie Brandt
Tom Bratt
Cody Braun
Joseph Braun
Lauren Braun
Julie Braunstein
Julianne Breck
Cynthia Breckenridge

Trisha Breitlow
Lisa Brennan
Sean Brennan
Julia Brenner
Gavin Breyer
Holly Brinkman
Bailey Brittin
Will Broadway
Emily Brodman
Alyssa Brody
Megan Brody
Nicholas Broeker
Ben Broeren
Anne Brogden
Max Brooks
Alex Brower
Alexa Brown
Ryan Brown
Sarah Brown
Suzanne Broz
Brad Brubaker
Kyle Bruck
Lena Bruncaj
Taylor Buck
Emily Buckler
Fritz Buerger
Robin Buerki
Megan Burbank
Erica Burgess
Adam Burke
Claire Burke
Robin Burke
Eliza Burmester
Christian Burnham
Patrick Burns
Kate Burrows
Micki Burton
Alexis Buryk
Trent Busakowski
Amelia Buzzell

Mark Byrne
Dara Cahill
Jane Calayag
Greg Callozzo
Angie Calvin
Caryn Cammarata
Katherine Campbell
Bryan Campen
Daniel Camponovo
Salvador Campos
Clarke Canedy
Matthew Capdevielle
Debbie Capone
Meredith Carey
Elyse Caringella
Dan Carlin
Matthew Carmichael
Erin Carpenter
Val Carpenter
Pat Carr
Andrés Carrasquillo
Katie Carrico
Justin Carrino
Sarah Carson
Sean Carson
Jenna Carusa
Julia Carusillo
Shea Caruthers
Marty Casey
Linda Cassady
Moira Cassidy
Laura Castellano
Nina Castillo
Ramon Castillo
Ximena Castro
Lauren Catey
Christopher Caton
Brian Catt
Amy Cavanaugh
Pete Cavanaugh

Jane Cella
Stephanie Chacharon
Andrea Chadderdon
Walt Chadick
Sarah Chakrin
Katherine Champagne
Justine Chan
Sam Chavis
Mimi Cheng
Rosie Chevalier
Jessica Anne Chiang
Sharada Chidambaram
Marc Chima
Hannah Cho
Crystal Choi
Ashlee Christian
Anna Ciamporcero
Anthony Cipolla
Rachel Claff
Earl Clark
Matt Clark
Sebastian Clark
Stephanie Clark
Brenden Clarke
Kristin Clarke
Cassie Jo Cleary
Samantha Cleaver
Maura Clement
Christian Clouston
Elizabeth Coady
Tyler Coates
Liz Coda
Barbara Coe
Chrissy Cogswell-
Hyland
Gloria Cohen
Michael Cohen
Rick Cohen
Chloe Cole
Susan Cole

Erin Coleman
Kelly Coleman
Josh Collard
Lillian Colonna
Carrie Colpitts
Briana Colton
John Colucci
Amber Colvin
Nancy Conger
Caroline Conley
Janet Conneely
John Conneely
Dan Connelly
Sean Conner
Kelly Connolly
Joshua Connor
Jesse Connuck
Margot Considine
Peggy Cook
Chris Coons
David Cooper
Gabriella Cooper
Lydia Cooper
Elizabeth Cooperman
Julia Copeland
Laura Copelly
Kevin Corcoran
Jennifer Cordeau
Martin Cortez
Nicolas Cote
Chris Couch
Samantha Coulter
Mary Beth Hoerner
Nicholas Covey
Lauren Cowen
Susie Cowen
Katherine Craft
Nathan Craig
Margaret Cramer
Lindsay Crammond

Bridget Crawford
Kelsey Crick
Michael Croce
Jason Crock
Connie Croghan
Jeni Crone
Matthew Cronin
Maliea Croy
Colleen Cummings
Matthew Cunningham
Sheryl Curcio
Jordan Curnes
Michael Curran
Lisa Curtin
Ann Curtis
Jan Curtis
Matthew Cutler
Nada Cuvalo
Jon Cwiok

Michelle Czarnecki
Michael D'Agostino
Angela D'Agostinoe
Steven Dagdigian
Michelle Dahlenburg
Danielle Dahlin
Alison Daigle
Cima Dairanieh
Anne Danberg
Christina Daniels
Jennifer Daniels
Hali Danielson
Jennifer Danko
Stephen Danos
Jeanna Darby
Sophia Darugar
Lauren Date
Chris Davidson
Staci Davidson
Angelica Davila
Debra Davis

Jared Davis
Lindsay Davis
Lisa Davis
Grayson Daskawicz-Davis
Alysha Daytner
Marco De La Rosa
Ann Marie Dvorak De Morales
Alex De Raadt St. James
Claire DeBoer
Kate DeBuys
Shauna Dee
Ben Defalco
Kristin Dehaan
Evelyn Dehais
Michelle Deiermann
Jon Deitemyer
Vivian Delgadillo
Amy DeLorenzo
Dana Demas
Christine DeMonte
Joe Dempsey
Holly DeMuth
Emily Dennison
Rishi Desai
Laurie Desch
Natalie Desjardins
Meredith Desmond
Sally Deupree
Thomas Devine
Rachel Devitt
Alana DeVoe
Dawn Dewald
Heather DeWar
Brijeet Dhaliwal
Martha Diamond
Catherine Diao
Paul Dichter

Cara Dickason
Karina Diehl
Catherine Dierker
Stephen Dierks
Genevieve Diesing
Molly Dillon
Tonya Dills
Jillian Dimas
Mia DiMeo
Joe DiRago
Mike Dobias
Peter 'Mac' Dobson
Laura Dockterman
Sarah Dolan
Jen Donahue
Rory Donnelly
Brandon Dorn
Jonathan Doster
Nicole Dotto
James Dougherty
Courtney Douglas
Jesse Dow
Karrie Dowling
James Doyle
Jonathan Doyle
Lisa Doyle
Sarah Doyle
Erin Drain
Sarah Drake
Sylvia Drake
Sarah Drehobl
Emily Dresslar
Karen Dreyfuss
David Driscoll
Joe Drogos
Brendan Dry
Jill Dryer
Tara Dubbs
Theresa Duffy
Molly Dull

Alex Dunbar
Conrad Duncker
Heather Dunkel
Ellen Dunn
Holly Dunsworth
David Dworin
Gunn Dwyer
David Dyer
Jennifer Dyer
Molly Each
Lindsay Eanet
Christopher Earnhart
Steve Eastwood
Ellie Eaton
Sarah Ebel
Sara Edelstein
Mollie Edgar
D.R. Edwards
Libby Egan
Zoelle Egner
Jason Eiben
Elia Einhorn
Thomas Einstein
Arthur Eith
Molly Ekerdt
Jennifer Elder
Alexia Elejalde-Ruiz
Ali Elkin
Libby Ellis
Brooke Ellison
David Emanuel
Michelle Embleton
Ilana Emer
Monica Eng
Gillian Engberg
Sebastian Enguidanos
Ian Epstein
Kristin Esch
Steven Etheridge
Ben Etherington

Jeanne Ettelson
Michael Eugenio
Jesse Evans
Kim Evans
Andrea Everman
Bobby Evers
Mike Ewing
Thales Exoo
Erica Faaborg
Lisa Fairman
Brendan Faloona
Monica Fambrough
Molly Fannin
Amanda Faraone
Manal Farhan
Laura Farina
Brianne Farley
Maureen Farley
Hailey Fasse
Nicole Faust
Mary Fay
Anna Fehsenfeld
Paul Fermin
Bentley Ford Ferraina
Caitlin Ferrara
Brittney Ferrero
Kristine Fetalo
Chelsea Fiddyment
Chloe Fields
Rachel Fields
Maria Filippone
Marisol Finch
Adam Findlay
June Finfer
Mollie Firestone
Rachel Fischhoff
Holly Fisher
Joyce Fisher
Brendon Fitzgerald
Elizabeth Fitzgerald

John Flaherty
Amy Flamenbaum
Anne Flanagan
Joe Fleischhacker
Lisa Floran
Dyan Flores
Katie Flores
James Flynn
Matthew Flynn
Maura Foley
Ahndria Ford
Anne Ford
Alice Foreman
Sandy Forkins
Lynne Fort
Kalman Fortoloczki
Abby Foster
Donald Fostner
Jenna Fowler
Justin Fowler
Ariel Fox
Jodi Fox
Josh Fox
Laura Fox
Nora Fox
Vincent Francone
Amelia Frank
Alysha Frankel
Colleen Frankhart
Nicole Franks
Jaime Freedman
Madeleine Freeman
Sarah Freeman
Alex Frenkel
Jessica Friedman
Sarah Frier
Kenneth Froehlig
Andee Fromm
Katharine Fronk
Ian Fullerton

Duayne Fulton
Jacky Fung
Adam Gaeddert
LeAnn Gaines
Shawn Gaines
Lindsay Galan
April Galarza
Brian Gallagher
Katy Gallagher
Maureen 'Mo'
Gallagher
Terry Gallagher
Irene Gallego-Romero
Ashley Gallegos
Jessica Galli
Genevra Gallo-Bayiates
Grisel Gamboa
Shawn Gancarz
Susanne Gannon
Amy Ganser
Daniela Garcia
Nicholas Gardner
Lizzie Garnett
Kevin Garvey
Heather Gately
Alyxandra Gauthier
Hoku Gearheard
Mike Gebel
Jennifer Gebhardt
James Geisen
Sherri Geng
Amy Gentry
Brian George
Jason Gerken
Megan Gerrity
Matt Getz
Samay Gheewala
Allyson Gibbs
Gil Gibori
Erik Giles

Lauren Gill
Jennifer Gillespie
Diane Gillette
Cassandra Gillig
Katy Githens
Ellen Gladish
Julie Glassman
Jeb Gleason-Allured
Tom Gleiber
Anne Glickman
Jeannie Glickson
Elizabeth Goetz
Natalie Goldstein
Sharyn Goldyn
Krystin Gollihue
Ursula Gomez-
Hamilton
Renee Goodenow
Jeff Goodman
Brad Gookins
James Gordon
Jeremy Gordon
Jessica Gordon
Molly Gore
Katya Gorecki
JP Gorman
Sathya Gosselin
Mark Gotfredson
Ian Gould
Sharon Graboys
Shannon Grady
Caitlin Graham
Clayton Graham
Sarah Grainer
Alison Grant
Phylicia Grant
Heather Gray
Lisa Grayson
Haley Green
Kent Green

Abigail Greenbaum
Deborah Greenberg
Hannah Greene
Janelle Greene
Sara Greenewalt
Rachel Greenfield
Katie Greenock
David Alex Greenwald
Brian Gregg
Stacey Grieff
Matthew Grimaldi
Joe Grimberg
Ben Groch
Nora Gross
Rachel Gross
Miriam Grossman
Jason Grotto
Jess Grover
Katy Groves
Peter Groves
Carrie Grucz
Eric Gueller
Carol Guerra
Yessica Guerrero
Michelle Guittar
Brian Gulotta
Saumya Gumidyala
Justin Gumiran
Priyanka Gupta
Claire Guyer
Tran Ha
Audrey Haberman
Tom Hackney
Victoria Haddad
Theodore Hahn
Lynn Haller
Nicole Halm-Lutterodt
Katie Halpern
Paul Halupka
Abbey Hambright

Jared Hamilton
Sophia Hamilton
Charles
Hammerslough
Terry Han
Rachel Handler
Keegan Hankes
Colette Hannahan
Katie Hannon
Suzie Hanrahan
Kirsten Hansen
Kory Hansen
Steve Hanson
Mike Hanus
Reina Hardy
Devon Hargrove
Deven Hariyani
Benjamin Harmon
Brandon Harper
Jeanne Harrell
Patrick Harrington
Bradley Harris
Leah Harris
Shawna Harris
Kathleen Harsy
Bobby Hart
Erica Hart
Jessica Hart
Boris Hartl
Lawrence Hartmann
Alicia Harvey
Steven Hasday
Evelyn Haselden
Wally Hasselburg
Briggs Hatton
Megan Hauser
Laura Hawbaker
Maysan Haydar
Scott Hayden
Emily Hayes

Lane Hayjack
Nicole Haysler
Andrew Hayward
Helen Hazlett
Shuhan He
Amy Heather
Charles Hebert
Laurel Hechanova
Matt Hedley
Ryan Heer
Dan Hefner
Marisa Heilman
Anna Heinemann
Steve Heisler
Libby Hemphill
Rich Henderson
Brendan Hendrick
Marie Hendrickson
Marissa Heneghan
Julia Heney
Aubrey Henretty
Laurie Hensley
Theresa Hercher
Jennifer Herlein
Catherine Herman
Jessica Herman
Nicole Herman
Sari Hernandez
Seth Herr
Angelica Herrera
Gerardo Herrera
Brendan Herrig
Lesley Hershman
Charlie Hershow
Arianna Hess
Laura Hess
Clare Hiatt
Patrick Hicks
Maureen Hickey
Anne Marie Nist

Sarah Higgins
Carolyn Highland
Brian Hildebrand
Katie Hill
Rebecca Hill
Sheri Hillson
Kareem Hindi
Katheryn Hines
Kim Hines
Dan Hinkel
Franz Hinojosa
Emily Hippert
Allie Hirsch
Jeremy Hirsch
Jason Hissong
Stephanie Hlywak
Amanda Hobbs
Hilary Hodge
Mary Beth Hoerner
David Hoffman
Wayne Hoffman
Linda Hogan
Liza Hogan
Tim Hogan
Victoria Hohenzy
Daniel Hollander
Amy Hollinger
Debbie Holm
Crystal Holmes
Sarah Holtkamp
Anne Holub
Julia Hon
Akemi Hong
Ginger Hood
Andrew Hook
Laura Hool
Tess Hopey
David Howard
Jerrod Howe
Jill Howe

Dani Hoyler
Constance Hsu
Albert Huber
Steve Hudson
Bob Huguelet
Kimberly Hula
Andrew Humphries
Wendy Hush
Thomas Hutch
Rebecca Huval
Brit Hvide
Cathy Hwang
Danielle Hyde
Jason Hyde
Annie Hynick
Anthony Iamurri
Caroline Imreibe
Allison Isaacson
Noah Isackson
Larissa Itomlenskis
Katie Itterman
Daniel Ivec
Brenna Ivey
Jeff Jablonski
Anna Jackson
Paul Jackson
Whitney Jackson
Jonathan Jacobson
Shama Jacover
Susan Jaffee
Mike Jamoom
Joe Janes
Stephanie Janisch
Alex Janiuk
Nick Janquart
Jaclyn Jansen
Anton Janulis
Abbie Jarman
Jessica Jarrett
Robert Jasenof

Alexandra Jasura-
Semer
Ben Javellana
Rachel Javellana
Kiley Jeffery
Jac Jemc
Andrea Jennings
Kellie Jensen
Matt Jensen
Naomi Baz Jensen
Peter Jensen
Sara Jensen
Justine Jentes
Drew Jerdan
Sarah Jersild
Cristina Jimenez
Gabi Jirasek
Jennifer Johannesen
Adam Johns
Amanda Johnson
Aral Johnson
Bryan Johnson
Ian Johnson
Jeff Johnson
Joan Johnson
Kevin Johnson
Lindsey Johnson
Melissa Johnson
Rachel Johnson
Valerie Johnson
Zenia Johnson
Stephanie Jokich
Emily Jones
Katie Jones
Levi Jones
Liz Jones
Scott Jones
Siggy Jonsson
Jessica Joseph
Jim Joyce

Thomas Joyner
Allison Judy
Vera Junge
John Kaderbek
Sara Kagay
Melanie Kahl
Kirsten Kahlo
Nora Kahn
Erin Kahua
Fergus Kaiser
Tamara Kaldor
Rebecca Kallemeyn
Kunal Kalro
Julie Kalsow
Roger Kamholz
Kari Kamin
Rachel Kamins
Brian Kane
Kyungmin Kang
Jon Kaplan
Phil Kaplan
Kate Karczewski
Jason Karley
Kimya Karshenas
Kyle Kartz
Erin Kasdin
Andrea Kasprzak
Paul Kastner
LaCoya Katoe
Lydia Katsamberis
Lara Kattan
Bonnie Katz
Rebecca Katz
Jenny Kauchak
Adam Kauffman
Shayne Kavanagh
Nick Kawahara
Michelle Kaye
Bob Kazel
Clare Kealy

Erin Keane
Meghan Keedy
Michelle Keefe
Phillip Keefe
Arianne Keegan
Juliana Keeping
Cam Keitel
Maureen Kelleher
Beth Keller
Craig Keller
Allison Kelley
Joanna Kelley
Taylor Kelley
Ami Kelly
Dan Kelly
Matt Kelly
Rob Kenagy
Anne Kenealy
Annie Kennedy
Krista Kennedy
Eric Kenron
Chad Kenward
Sarah Keough
Bonnie Kepplinger
Rian Kerfoot
Alison Kesler
Wesley Ketcham
Meghan Keys
Faraaz Khan
Oliver Khan
Trisha Khanna
Jean Khut
Amy Leigh Kile
Christine Kim
Debbie Kim
Lisa Kim
Sharon Kim
Susannah Kim
Yehsong Kim
Hayley Kimbrue

Kathryn King
Sasha Kinney
Nicolette Kittinger
Adam Kivel
Phillip Klapperich
Katy Klassman
Joan Klaus
Julie Kleczek
Victoria Klimaj
Andrew Kline
Steve Klise
Katie Klocksin
Allison Kloiber
Kristopher Knabe
Alicia Knapp
Samuel Knewstub
Emily Knies
Jamie Knight
Sarah Knight
Ellen Knuti
Rachel Ko
Erin Koch
Mitchell Kohles
Felicity Kohn
Lorie Kolak
Annika Konrad
Shelly Koop
Katrina Kopeck
Andy Kopsa
Demetrios Korakis
Mike Koralik
Kaytey Korwitts
Fred Koschmann
Rebecca Kosick
Julie Koslowsky
Alex Kostiw
Kate Kraft
Sonia Kraftson
Melody Kramer
Maria Krasinski

Corinne Kritikos
Lisa Krobuchar
Eric Kroh
Megan Krone
Beth Kruger
Amy Krzyzek
Alison Kuczwara
Danielle Kuffler
Lindsay Kundel
Josh Kurlander
Dan Kuruna
Camille Kuthrell
Leanna Kutzer
Martii Kuznicki
Jennie Kwon
Liz Ladach-Bark
Monte LaForti
Nathalie Lagerfeld
Danielle LaGrippe
Nicole Lalich
Christina Lalli
Maria Lalli
Dika Lam
Katherine Lamp
Jon Lamphere
Andrew Lampl
Dave Landsberger
Melissa Lane
Emily Lang
Matt Lang
Jessi Langsen
Joe Lanter
Kellyn Lappinga
Alison Lara
Liz Larrimore
Brandi Larsen
Matt Larsen
Jordan Larson
Julie Larson
Laura Lash

Mark Lask
Paul Lask
Kate Later
Michael Latham
Madeline Lau
Mallory Laurel
Ian Law
Megan Lawler
Conrad Lawrence
Kate Lawroski
Alicia Layton
Chris Le
Kristin Leahey
Nathan Leahy
Jessica Leary
Margaret Lebron
Phil Lederer
Ed Lee
Julie Lee

Mark Lee
Kevin Leeds
Heather Leet
Michael Lehman
Zoe Lehman
Alison Lehner
Katie Leimkuehler
Aaron Leiva
Elizabeth Lenaghan
Anthony Lenhart
Cesar Lerma
Jonathan Lesser
Josh Lesser
Jessica Levco
Rachel Levi
Stephanie Levi
Natalie Levin
Gabriel Levinson
Hayley Levitan
Larissa Levitan
Brian Lewis-Jones

Grace Lewis
Hilary Lewis
Lauren Lewis
Kaity Li
Bret Libigs
Rebecca Liddy
Janisse Lifton
Aimee Light
Kristina Lilleberg
Vicky Lim
Teresa Lin
Erica Lindberg
Lia Lindsey
John Link
Robin Linn
Jamison Linz
Mike Lipka
Amy Lipman
Erica Lipper
Kathryn Lisinicchia
Erin Little
Danielle Littman
Sharon Lo
Julia Lobo
Mary Loftus
Alyson Lokken
Elizabeth London
Kevin Longstreth
Anna Loosli
Sam Lopata
Michele Lopatin
Brian Lopez
Morgan Lord
Lesley Loreh
Joseph Lorenzo
Elena Losey
Elizabeth Loudermilk
Meredith Lovelace
Lauren Lowe
Rhonda Lowry

Andrew Lubetkin
Janet Lubetkin
Maura Lucking
Sarah Luczko
Kristin Lueke
Stuart Luman
Oren Lund
Rebecca Lund
Samantha Lundequam
Jessica Lunney
Tricia Lunt
Jean Luo
Anthony 'AJ' Lupie
Annie Lydgate
Shianne Lyles
Laura Lytle
Faren MacDonald
Caitlin MacDougall
Nikki Macey
Sandy Machugin
Colin MacLaughlin
Chris Mack
Sophia Madana
Hisham Madani
Amy Madden
Tanya Madison-Ogboi
Jessica Madsen
Erinrose Mager
Beth Maggard
Gabriel Magliaro
Tim Magner
Christine Magnotta
Laura Forster
Maheshwary
Ellen Mahon
Ben Majoy
Rohit Malhotra
Saarah Malik
Jason Malikow
Daniel Mallory

Danielle Malloy
Colleen Malone
Jay Malone
Colin Maloney
Patricia Maloney
Charles Malueg
Dianne Malueg
Erika Manczak
Jerry Mandujano
Daniel Mann
Jonathan Mannheim
Shaun Manning
Katie Marcuz
Rebecca Margolis
Eric Margulies
Sado Marinovic
Stephen Markley
James Markus
Clay Markwell
Jenna Marotta
Jessica Marsh
Maya Marshall
Jessica Martell
Elizabeth 'Betsy'
Martens
Lizzie Martin
Nate Martin
Alyssa Martinez
Deanna Martinez
Kaitlyn Marx
David Mason
Galen Mason
Scott Mason
Lisa Massura
Timothy Masterton
Jeff Matheis
Amanda Mather
Amber Matheson
Emily Matis
Andrew Matson

Tasha Matsumoto
Lex Mattera
Meredith Matthews
Tamara Matthews
Thomas Matysik
Aaron Maurer
Paula Mauro
Miranda Max
Alisa Mazur
Liz Mazur
Jessica Mazza
Jordan McAllister
Andrea McCabe
Liz McCabe
Jennifer McCafferty
Chris McCaughan
Katie McCaughan
Andrew McClain
Meghan McCook
Kelly McCurdy
Bronwyn McDaniel
Joselyn McDonald
Morgan McDonald
Brennan McDowell
Essence McDowell
Margaret McEachern
Bridget McFadden
Molly McGee
Catherine McGeeney
Sherry McGuire
Tom McHenry
Maureen McHugh
Becka McKay
Kerri McKeand
Sean Mckee
Elizabeth McKeon
Erin McMahan
Ellen McMahon
Victoria McManus
Sarah McMurrough

Sean McMurrough
Jessica McNaughton
Paula McNicholas
Heather McShane
Jennifer McSurley
Bronwyn Mead
James Meador
Joy Meads
Jay Meerbaum
Rudy Mehrbani
Neha Mehta
Jordan Meinholz
Carole Meiselman
Chris Meister
Meredith Melragon
Sarah Meltzer
Jason Menard
Heather Menefee
Rob Mentzer
Sergio Mercado
Megan Mercer
Sarah Merchlewitz
Carrie Messenger
Betsy Messimer
Lynn Metz
Vaughan Meyer
Vida Mikalcius
Betsy Mikel
Naomi Millan
Bob Miller
David Miller
Eric Miller
Hayley Miller
Jolene Miller
Lindsey Miller
Margaret Miller
Rose Miller
Rubin Miller
Megan Milliken
Shannon Milliken

169

Maximilian Millington
Jessica Milnaric
Max Minor
Bethany Minton
Chris Mitchell
Laura Mittelstaedt
Mark Mitten
Jane Moccia
Sally Moeller
Anne Moertel
Pat Mohr
Rachel Moldauer
Steve Molnar
Dan Monaghan
Catherine Monahan
Kendra Monroe
Megan Monroe
Moises Montenegro
Kate Montgomery
Lily Mooney
Heidi Moore
Martine Moore
Natalie Moore
Nora Moore
Paul Moore
Michael Moreci
CJ Morello
Ross Moreno
Meredith Morgan
Tina Morgan
Alyssa Morin
Sondra Morin
Hubert Moring
Nika Morley
Emily Moroni
Amanda Morris
Emily Morrison
Robin Morrissey
Jason Mortensen
Michael Mortitz

Alan Morua
Caroline Mosely
David Moskowitz
Jessie Moskowitz
John Moss
Kat Mounts
Mark Moyes
Joe Moylan
Rozanna Mroz
Corinne Mucha
Moira Muldowney
April Muller
Courtney Muller
Erik Mullner
Tracy Mumford
Michael Munley
Jennifer Munn
Caitlin Murphy
Hugh Musick
Kevin Musiorski
Colleen Muszynski
Dana Muvceski
Benjamin Nadler
Sandy Naing
Nathan Nanfelt
Vineeth Narayanan
Elizabeth Narrish
Courtney Nash
Kelsey Nash
Andrew Naughtie
Paulina Nava
Troy Nee
Anna Neher
Elizabeth Neiman
Susanne Nelsen
Alyson Nelson
Blake Nelson
Jennifer Nelson
John Nelson
Michelle Nelson

Regina Nelson
Rick Ness
John Neurater
Marielle Newman
Hannibal Newsom
Dan Nguyen
Lance Nicholls
Kris Nielsen
Chris Niemyjski
Mary Beth Stanton
Michael Nitschky
Cole Nonderee
Tara Noonan
Alexis Nordling
Aimee Norkett
Caty Norman-Burke
Jason Norris
Rachel Notor
Tricia Nowacki
Sarah Nun
Carla Nuzzo
Amanda Nyren
John O'Brien
Lindsey O'Brien
Mara O'Brien
Kyle O'Connell
Steve O'Connell
Kim O'Connor
Amy O'Daniel
Nora O'Donnell
Brian O'Grady
Sean O'Leary
Kat O'Meara
Larry O'Meara
Dan O'Neil
Katie-Anne O'Neil
Danielle O'Young
Katie Obriot
Amy Odenthal
Nancy Odisho

Kate Ogden
Onyekachi Okoroafor
Brooke Olaussen
Dana Oliveri
April Olsen
Scott Onak
Chris Oposnow
Elizabeth Ordonez
Sidera Origer
Lori-May Orillo
Elizabeth Orlando
Joey Orr
Josh Orr
Maurya Orr
Kristin Orser
Beth Osborn
Franz Osorio
Jacqueline Ostrowski
Jacob Otting
Rachel Otto
Marc Ovies
Barry Owen
Colin Packard
Jen Page
Christopher Palafax
Jessica Palmer
Michael Palmer
Monica Palmer
Tom Palmer
Peggy Panosh
Melanie Pappadis
Liz Pardee
Kate Paris
Daniel Park
Dustin Park
Frances Park
Laura Park
Rachel Park
Trevor Park
Benjamin Parker

Brandy Parker
Diana Parker
Jeffrey Parker
Rebecca Parker
Scott Parker
Scott Parker
Andrew Parkinson
Dustin Parmenter
Ford Parsons
Monique Parsons
Ashley Pastore
Brigid Pasulka
Bindiya Patel
Krupa Patel
Sheila Patel
Gavin Paul
Laura Pearson
Frances Peebles
Tilghman Pelczar
Valerie Pell
Kate Pemberton
Amy Pemble
Emily Penn
Christopher Penna
Emmet Penney
Laura Perelman
Brad Perkins
Karen Perkins
Becky Perlman
Rebecca Pernic
Leslie Perrine
Halcyon Person
Aisha Pervaiz
Emi Peters
Kristin Peters
Evan Peterson
Krissy Peterson
Michael Peterson
Dan Petrella
Sammuel Petrichos

Kristen Petrillo
Conor Pewarski
Jenny Pfafflin
Sadie Pfannkuche
Ashley Pflaumer
Soukprida Phetmisy
Laura Philbin
Mary Philips
Cassie Phillips
Kelly Phillips
Shelby Phillips
Joan Philo
Johna Picco
Carli Pierce
Meagan Pierce
Erik Pierson
Megan Pietrantonio
Brynna Pietz
Jane Piglianelli
Seshini Pillay
Julianna Pinnaro
Joseph Pizzolato
Lee Plaxco
Joi Podgorny
Claire Podulka
Susan Pogash
Sarah Polen
Anne Polick
David Pompei
Jade Popson
Matthew Porubcansky
Chelsea Potter
Janet Potter
Emily Power
Laura Power
Augie Praley
Dan Prazer
Matthew Present
Kimberly Priebe
Tom Priebe

Allison Pritchard	Dane Reighard	Merritt Robinson
Billie Pritzker	Brittany Reilly	Tony Robinson
Kate Prockovic	Moira Reilly	Mary Robnett
Lydia Pudzianowski	Craig Reinbold	Allison Roche
Kamala Puligandla	Breanne Reindl	Jenny Roche
Aparna Puppala	Natalie Reinhart	Aine Rock
Tiana Pyer-Pereira	Philipp Rejmer	Kathleen Rockwell
Rebecca Pyles	Angie Renfro	Scott Rodd
Michael Quan	Aaron Renier	Barbra Rodichok
Courtney Queeney	Daniel Resner	Cristina Rodriguez
Christine Quinn	Courtney Reynolds	Kristina Rodriguez
Drennen Quinn	Jeffery Rhodes	Laura Roeder
Thomas Quinn	Julia Rice	Clint Rogers
Akasha Rabut	Mae Rice	Cynthia Rogowski
Lisa Radecki	Mary Richards	Blair Rohrbach
Sara Radin	Ramona Richards	Catherine Rolfe
Heather Radke	Matthew Richardson	Jennifer Rolniak
Brian Rady	Allison Rickard	Perry Romanowski
Daniel Raeburn	Erin Riddick	Shannon Romanowski
Nandita Raghuram	Christopher Rife	Chiarita Rose
Anne Raih	Analiese Riga	Noelle Rose
Diana Raiselis	Megan Riggle	Ellen Rosen
Vicki Rakowski	Anna Rinaldi	Naomi Rosen
Megha Ralapati	Mandy Rinder	Robert Rosen
Clarisa Ramirez	Allison Ringhand	Ben Rosenberg
David Ramos	Jessica Ripper	Andy Rosenstein
Genevieve Ramos	Sam Ritchey	Amy Krouse Rosenthal
Scott Randel	Adena Rivera-Dundas	Christina Rosetti
Cyrus Rashtchian	Katja Rivera	Brian Ross
Amy Ravenhorst	Kelly Rix	Benjamin Rossi
Amol Ray	Paul Rizzuto	Joshua Rothhaas
Lucy Raymond	Alice Robbins	Jesse Rothschild
Mariel Razalan	Jesse Robbins	Annie Rothstein
Katie Reardon	Jane Roberti	Adam Roubitchek
Laura Reasons	Kayleigh Roberts	Amanda Rowe
Derek Reed	Lynne Roberts	Peggy Rowland
Gail Reich	Helena Robertson	Sumit Roy
Rebecca Reid	Kellie Robertson	Ben Rubenstein
Monica Reida	Annie Robinson	Adam Rubin
Dave Reidy	Dana Robinson	Joshua Ruddy

Joanna Rudenborg
Jessica Rudis
Annie Rudnik
Michele Rudoy
Amy Ruff
Alyssa Rusak
Nina Rusiecki
Molly Russell
Peter Russell
Megan Ruthaivilavan
Adam Rux
Sara Ruzomberka
Claire Ryan
Erin Ryan
Kyle Ryan
Megan Ryan
Mike Sack
Kim Sagami
Meggen Saka
Dave Salanitro
Brian Sallade
Kelsey Salmen
Craig Salvona
Tyler Samples
April Samuelson
Emily Sandberg
Peter Sander
Cassy Sanders
Emilie Sandoz
Elizabeth SanFilipo
John Santore
Shannon Sapolich
Paige Sarlin
Alena Saunders
Cheryl Saurber
Claire Savage
Brandy Savarse
Megan Saxelby
John Saxton
Christine Sayers

Kathryn Scanlan
Harry Schechter
Jennifer Schelewitz
Laura Schell
Renee Schildgen
Erika Schmidt
Cassandra Schmutz
James Schneider
Stephanie Schoenen
Amy Schoenhals
Rachael Scholten
Jillian Schrager
Michael Schramm
Matt Schrecengost
Julie Schriefer
Kate Schriner
Leigh Schrock
James Schroeder
Jason Schrowe
Matt Schuenke
Marjorie Schuetz
Timothy Schuler
Sam Schulhfer-Wohl
Kelly Schultz
Stacy Schultz
Steve Schultz
Matt Schumake
Brynn Schwaba
Erica Schwanke
Abby Schwarz
Liz Scordato
Amanda Scotese
Lesley Scott
Mark Scott
Jordan Scrivner
Stephanie Seagle
Javier Sedillo
Carly Seguin
Laura Selby
Elizabeth Self

Shauna Seliy
Melissa Semeh
Jessica Server
Romulo Severino
Melissa Sevilla
Julie Shaffner
Paras Shah
Kashif Shaikh
Anthony Shaker
Lisa Shames
Daniel Shapiro
Jordan Shappell
Rachel Green Sharpe
Sean Shatto
Diane Shaughnessy
Frank Shaw
Allyson Shea
Kristin Sheehan
Vanessa Sheehan
Emily Shepard
Anne Shepherd
Kristine Sherred
Doug Shetterly
John Shonkwiler
Laura Short
Stephen Shoup
Emily Shultz
Merissa Shunk
Andrea Silenzi
Lia Silver
Jessica Sime
Katie Simon
Steve Simoncic
Paul Simpson
Gabrielle Sinclair
Matt Singer
Sarah Singer
Gogi Singh
Patrick Sisson
Margaret Sivit

173

Sarah Skerrett
Lauren Skinner
Maggie Skoller
Justin Skolnick
Mahrinah Slagle
Molly Slavin
Jason Sloat
Amanda Slone
Annie Slotnick
Erin Slucter
Allen Smart
Caitlyn Smith
Claire Smith
David Smith
Derrick Smith
Jeremy Smith
Kyle Smith
Laura Smith
Nicole Smith
Pete Smith
Sarah Smith
Sarah Smith
Troy Smothers
Anna Smunt
Amy Snickenberger
Anna Snickenberger
Danielle Snow
Marie Snyder
Lisa Soare
Alex Soble
Kate Soderberg
Abraham Sohn
Brian Solem
Sarah Soler
Dan Solomon
Elaine Soloway
Chresten Sorensen
Kate Soto
Raquel Soto
Natalie Southwick
Marissa Spalding

Kathryn Spangler
Kevin Sparrow
Cecilia Sperry
Jed Spiegelman
Chelsea Sprayregen
Michelle Springer
Victoria Sroka
Caitlin Stainken
Justin Staley
Elizabeth Stamberger
Julia Stamberger
Kati Stanford
Debbie Stanley
Kelly Stanley
Lesley Stanley
Mary Beth Stanton
Lee Stark
Jennifer Statler
Peter Steadman
Kim Steele
Meg Steele
Camilla Stefl
Amelia Stegall
Emma Steimel
Chelsea Lane Walls
Noah Stein
Julia Steinberger
Sierra Sterling
Arianna Stern
Natalie Sternberg
Smith Steve
John Stevens
Katie Stevens
Shawn Stevens
Dana Stewart
Juell Stewart
Wendy Stewart
Sarah Beth Warshauer
Chris Stiles
Derek Stiles
Wayne Stiles

Sarah Stoehr
Wes Stokes
Ellen Stolar
Laryssa Stolarskyj
Rachel Stone
Jon Stookey
Scarlett Stoppa
Benjamin Strauss
Jen Strauss
Karyn Strauss
Cierra Strawder
James Strzelinski
Brenna Stuart
Hana Suckstorff
Matt Sudman
John Suh
Cayenne Sullivan
Karen Sullivan
Marin Sullivan
Megan Sullivan
Peter Sullivan
John Sundlof
Shirley Sung
Sejal Sura
Chamberlin Susan
Gregory Sussman
Mark Sussman
Erika Svenningsen
Allison Swade
Orion Swann
Beth Swierczewski
T.J. Szafranski
Mark Szczuka
Nick Szewczyk
Ryan Tacata
Daniel Tafelski
Mary Tallon
Sheera Talpaz
Laura Tan
Diana Tang
Bill Tanner

Jessica Tansey
Anna Tarkov
Michael Tatman
Peter Tavolacci
Taryn Tawoda
Sally Taylor
Patty Templeton
Allison Tenn
Alex Tenorio
Brandon Terrell
Hector Terrence
John Theisen
Stuart Thiel
Karen Thimell
Matthew Thom
Andrea Thomalla
Alexis Thomas
Negetarian Thomas
Annie Thompson
Francesca Thompson
Ryan Thompson
Kara Thorstenson
John Thurgood
Jesse Thurston
Francisco Tirado
Lisa Marie Courtney
Kate Tkacik
Melissa Tobler
Cameron Todd
Erin Toolis
Kevin Toomey
Elise Topinka
Adam Torres
Taryn Towoda
Nicole Trafton
Vy Tran
Adam Travis
Jeffrey Treem
Le Trieu
Louise Tripp
Lisa Trudeau

Alison True
Elite Truong
Jennifer Tsang
Gwen Tulin
Peter Tulloch
George Tully
Melissa Turner
Nicole Twardzik
Susan Twetten
Julie Tymorek
Kate Udovicic
Holly Ulasovich
Bora Un
David Unger
Lara Unnerstall
Rufus Urion
Thomas Urwin
Daniel Usellis
Karen Uselmann
Aaqib Usman
Kimberly Vachon
Liz Vadas
Dave Vadeboncoeur
David Valento
Lila Valinoti
Whitney Van Arsdall
Stien Van Der Ploeg
Jon Van Hofwegen
Rebecca Van Horn
Paul Van Slembrouck
Eric VanDemark
Sarah Vanderah
Mark Vanderhoff
Joe Vandev
Delna Weil
Heahter Weiler
Kate Weinberg
Andrea Weinfurter
Matthew Weingast
Lindsey Weis
Jessica Weisberg

Tracy Weisman
Jeremy Weiss
Danielle Weissberg
Greg Weissel
Sandor Weisz
Tyler Wellington
Jen Welsing
Jaclyn Welstein
Zoe Wendel
Ryan Wenzler
Kathleen Wenzlick
Fabiola Werlang
Sarah Werner
Tomasz Werner
Winter Werner
Joshua Werth
Joshua Westlund
Lauren Wetherbee
Patty Wetli
Susanna Weyandt
Megan Wheeler
Aaron White
Ana White
Bryan White
Cate White
Henry White
Natalie White
Ashley Whitehurst
Thomas Whittington
Lindsay Wickman
Tom Wierzbinski
Jessica Wigent
Seth Wilde
Emily Wilensky
Crystal Williams
Ryan Williams
Stephanie Williams
Karl Williamson
John Wilmes
Brandon Wilner
Anna Wilson

175

Colleen Wilson
Jeremy Wilson
Kea Wilson
Lauren Wilson
Lisa Wilson
Ryan Wilson
Shannon Wilson
Stefanie Wilson
Elizabeth Winkowski
Emily Winter
Anne Wirtz
Max Wise
Rachel Wiseman
Jim Withington
Ryan Witthans
Jennifer
Wojciechowski
Jacy Wojcik
David Wolinsky

Cynthia Wong
Megan Wood
Tracy Woodley
Don Woods
Tanisha Woodson-
Shelby
Renee Woodward
Scott Worsham
Patrick Woyna
Elizabeth Wright
Mars Wright
Peter Wright
Carolyn Wrobel
Beth Wydler
Nora Wynn
Holly Wysel
Alexander Wysocki
Diana Xin
Robin Xu
Michelle (Susan) Yacht
Diane Yamazaki

Dave Yang
Prathima Yeddanapudi
Lena Yohey
Sarah Yoo
Laura Young
Emily Youseff
Nicki Yowell
Lauren Yurman
Haifa Zabout
Christina Zambon
Alfonso Zapataenter
Allison Vanek
Kylie Vanerstrom
Vedant Vasavda
Jaida Vaught
Aileen Keown Vaux
Asha Veal
Liliana Velazquez
Paula Velde
Julia Ventola
Brittany Verrette
Jennifer Verson
Alana Vest
Matt Vester
JoLynn Villaro
Terin Vintizil
Eugenia Viti
Evan Voboril
Erin Vogel
Mary Volk
Sera Vorpahl
Chris Wachal
Cari Wafford
Elizabeth Wagenschutz
A Jay Wagner
Gretchen Wahl
Mike Wakcher
Caroline Walker
Libby Walker
Ted Walker

Matthew Wallace
Jessica Anne Chiang
Erin Walter
Matt Walter
Rebecca Walz
Elizabeth Wampler
Dan Wang
Mike Warble
Steven Warmbir
Michelle Yacht
Anna Washenko
Jessica Wasserman
Rachel Watson
Nicky Way
Alex Wayman
Kristie Weaver
Erik Weber
Allison Weigel
Sally Weigel
Corin Zaragoza
Jan Zasowski
Shara Zaval
Jay Zawadzki
Sam Zelitch
Annie Zhou
Whitney Ziebarth
Nicole Zillmer
Laurna Zinger
Yvonne Zusel
Dina Zwiebel

ABOUT 826CHI

826CHI is a non-profit organization dedicated to supporting students ages 6 to 18 with their creative and expository writing skills, and to helping teachers inspire their students to write. Our services are structured around the understanding that great leaps in learning can happen with one-on-one attention, and that strong writing skills are fundamental to future success.

826CHI provides after-school tutoring, class field trips, writing workshops, and in-schools programs—all free of charge—for students, classes, and schools. All of our programs are challenging and enjoyable, and ultimately strengthen each student's power to express ideas effectively, creatively, confidently, and in his or her individual voice.

826CHI is one of eight chapters of 826 National, a nonprofit tutoring, writing, and publishing organization with locations in eight cities across the country. 826 Valencia, the flagship center in San Francisco, was founded by writer/editor Dave Eggers and educator Nínive Calegari in 2002. 826CHI opened its doors to Chicago students in October of 2005, joining 826 Valencia, 826LA, 826NYC, 826 Seattle, and 826michigan. In 2007, 826 Boston joined our national network of chapters and in 2010 we were excited to welcome 826DC.

OUR PROGRAMS

826CHI's free programs reach students at every opportunity—in school, after school, in the evenings, and on weekends.

After-School Tutoring and Writing

826CHI's site is packed four afternoons a week with students who come in for free one-on-one tutoring after school. We serve students of all skill levels and interests, most of whom live or go to school within walking distance of our writing center. Literacy is stressed through daily reading and daily projects at the Writing Table, as well as chapbook projects, where students' writing around a particular theme is compiled into small books and shared at family and community readings.

Field Trips

We want to help teachers get their students excited about writing while also helping students better express their ideas. 826CHI invites teachers to bring their students to our site for high-energy field trips during the school days. Teachers may choose from several field trip formats depending on their interests and grade level. A group of tutors is also on-hand during every field trip, whether we are helping to generate new material or revise already written work. The field trip program is so popular that our schedule is consistently filled almost a year in advance. To join our educator e-mail list to be notified when our registration for the next school year opens, please visit our website at **www.826chi.org**.

In-Schools

At a teacher's behest, we will send tutors into classrooms around the city to provide one-on-one assistance to students as they tackle various projects—Young Authors books, research papers, journalism projects, literary magazines, basic writing assignments, and college entrance essays. If you are a teacher interested in inviting our tutors into your classroom, please contact us through our website.

Workshops

826CHI offers free workshops that provide in-depth writing instruction in a variety of areas that schools often cannot include in their curriculum, such as college entrance essay writing, bookmaking, journalism, comic book making, playwriting, and songwriting. These innovative workshops allow students to hone and advance their skills while having fun and developing a greater sense of the joy of writing. All workshops are project-based and are taught by experienced, accomplished professionals and volunteers. Connecting Chicago students with these creative and generous mentors allows students to dream and achieve on a grand scale. Please visit our website to view our current workshop schedule.

Student Publishing

At 826CHI, we know the quality of student work is greatly enhanced when it is shared with an authentic audience. All of our activities are project-based, whether they result in an end-of-project book, a class performance, a gallery exhibit, a short film, or an exceptionally rockin' CD. As a writing center, we are especially committed to publishing student work for students to share with their friends, family, the public at-large, and the entire universe. Student publications may take the form of small chapbooks that we bind in-house or in professionally published volumes, such as this one. All forms of student publishing are available for purchase through The Boring Store.

826CHI shares its space with The Boring Store, Chicago's only undercover secret agent supply store. The Boring Store offers spy supplies in a highly-secretive way. We have grappling hooks, envelope x-ray spray, pigeon oil (if your carrier pigeon lacks luster), and an ever-expanding array of fake moustaches. Proceeds from The Boring Store go directly toward supporting 826CHI's programs for Chicago students. Can't risk being tailed by enemy agents? Have no fear. You can also conduct your highly classified operations online at **www.notasecretagentstore.com**.

Please visit us online at www.826chi.org or in-person at 1331 North Milwaukee Avenue in the Wicker Park neighborhood of Chicago to learn more about our programs and to find out how you can get involved.